¶ A descriptive list of some of the volumes in THE TRAVELLERS' LIBRARY will be found at the end of the volume.

¶ As further volumes are constantly being added to the Library, it is not always possible to keep these lists fully up to date. For the latest lists application should be made to any bookseller, or to the publishers.

FRIENDS IN SOLITUDE

by

PERCY WITHERS

WITH AN INTRODUCTION BY LASCELLES ABERCROMBIE

LONDON

JONATHAN CAPE 30 BEDFORD SQUARE

FIRST PUBLISHED 1923

FIRST ISSUED IN THE TRAVELLERS' LIBRARY 1930

PRINTED IN GREAT BRITAIN

Affectionately and reverently
TO THE MEMORY OF
ALICE MEYNELL
in the fourteenth year
of friendship

CONTENTS

Contents

Foreword

THEN spake Sir Frederick: I cannot denye you, Count Lewis, that writinge is not a maner of speaking. But this I saie, if the wordes that are spoken have any darkenesse in them, that communicacion perceth not the minde of him that heareth: and passing without being underſtoode, wexeth vaine and to no purpose: the whiche dothe not happen in writyng, for if the woordes that the writer useth bring with them a litle (I will not saie diffycultie) but covered subtilty, and not so open, as suche, as be ordinarily spoken, they geve a certain greater aucthoritye to writing, and make the reader more hedefull to pause at it, and to ponder it better. . . . And if the ygnoraunce of him that readeth bee suche, that he cannot compasse that difficultie, there is no blame in the writer, neither ought a man for all that to thinke that tunge not to bee faire.

HOBY'S *Courtier*

I am one of the few people in the world who do not forget their own lives.

R. L. STEVENSON

Life, that dares send
A challenge to the end,
And when it comes, say, " Welcome, friend."

R. CRASHAW

Introduction

Et ego in Arcadia vixi ! That, it seems to me, is my chief qualification for assuming the privilege of introducing this new edition of Mr. Percy Withers' "Friends in Solitude." Not, perhaps, a specially good qualification, since it is one which belongs equally well to a very large number of other people ; but at least it has enabled me to realize with what exquisite truth and unusual beauty Mr. Withers has described the sort of life which I, too, once enjoyed. Indeed, who that has ever had a long quiet spell of life in the country could help feeling the singular charm of this book ? It is not merely that he will find in it, rendered with sensitive art, feelings, reflexions, adventures, to which his own experience will delightedly respond ; what he will also find in it is a continual elucidation of his own pleasure. But the pleasure which Mr. Withers so finely elucidates is not to be known in week-ends or vacations ; nor by "life in the country" do I mean rural elegance and retired leisure, with punctual hot-water in the morning and the whole problem of fuel settled by writing a cheque for the coal merchant's bill. Mr. Withers' topic is the life of one who, escaping from the important bustle of town-affairs, "buried himself," as townsfolk say, for a considerable term of years in the country ; and as for fuel, that had to be provided for by exertions and dangers (since its transport, like the marketing, must be by water) which form the subject of one of the most engaging digressions in a book the unity of which consists in digressions. It is very much to my purpose to quote the final paragraph of this passage ; and it will serve as an example of Mr. Withers' command of prose-rhythm as well as of the delicate significance of his matter :

> Then the long unloading, the carrying up hill, the piling of the faggots, the stacking tent-wise of the baulks—these things all carried out with despatch during the afternoon, in readiness for the sawing and cleaving when the winter evenings came. And as memories, now I come to turn them over, to see them steadily and see them whole, I know not which I linger over most wistfully, those hours in the woods, the sunshine, the shadow, the laughter of children, or the woodyard in the dark evenings, with the wide door opening on to stars and gleaming waters, and within the scent of wood, the birling of the saw, and the lamplight falling on the pile of freshly hewn logs.

Now there you have it : there is the essence of life in the country. It is not merely that you live in the perpetual entertainment given by the round of the year, with all the interest that can be brought

vi.

under the name of "nature," the interest, nay, the excitement, that can never pall, because it never repeats itself. The real difference between town-life and country-life is just this : that in the town the ordinary, necessary commonplaces of life are indeed simple, nameless, unremembered acts ; they are mechanically done, they mean nothing but the mere doing of them and as soon as done they are dismissed. But in country life nothing is simple, everything is complicated by infinitely changeable circumstance, every act is an individual novelty, everything is memorable. In the town, you catch your bus, you do your shopping ; and forget it next day. In the country, you go to the post, you chop some wood ; and remember it all your life. To read Mr. Withers is to understand the secret of this difference.

But his book may be commended on more particular grounds. The life, of which it re-creates such pregnant memories in such admirable prose, was a period passed in that district which, for its mixture of natural beauty and human association, has no equal in England. No wonder it has become one of the chief playgrounds of the nation. But he must be a very insensitive visitor who does not feel that those who live year in, year out, in the Lake District, enjoy a mystery which the mere holiday-maker cannot expect to share by virtue of merely making holiday there. Yet he need not despair : literature can initiate him. It will not make him an adept ; but it can show him what life in the Lake District means, and the spirit which distinguishes it from any other kind of life. And the visitor to whom literature has revealed that spirit, will surely have a better holiday there than those who are content to come and gape and go. Obviously a great part of that revelation will be that sense of brotherhood with copse and fell and water which Faust longed to feel and which we, who know an enchantment Faust with all his magic could never compass, can experience in the poetry of Wordsworth. But life in the country would be a decidedly truncated affair if it merely consisted of brotherhood with "nature." The adepts have another secret from which the visitor is even more decisively excluded, unless, again, literature initiate him. You will never know what life in the Lake District truly means, until you know the minds and characters of the dalesfolk. Wordsworth will give you this too ; but you will get it, not indeed more profoundly, but certainly more easily, in greater variety, portrayed with richer particularity and more loving detail, from Mr. Withers. The people of the dales have never, to my knowledge, been better drawn. And nothing is more admirable, in the book as a whole, than the way Mr. Withers makes the sense of brotherhood with nature and the society of his neighbours interpenetrate one

viii.

another. The core of the book, indeed, is the figure of Peter Dalethwaite. Those who have been lucky enough to read Mr. Withers' former book, "In a Cumberland Dale," have already made acquaintance with that remarkable person ; but the sketch of him there is, in "Friends in Solitude," elaborated into a complete and singularly vivid portrait of the whole character of the man. Wordsworth often tells us how deeply all the circumstance of nature enters into the dalesman's mind and heart. Coleridge, who, though born in the country, had a thoroughly urban mind, did not believe this ; but those who have got to know Peter Dalethwaite with the intimacy which Mr. Withers' subtle and unobtrusive art procures for him, will find no difficulty in believing it. And Dalethwaite does not stand alone ; groupt round him are other figures of country life, each one making its peculiar impression on Mr. Withers' pages. Who that reads the account of Hardknotts meditating by the peaceful roadside his text for next Sunday's sermon —'O generation of vipers ! '—can possibly forget it ?

There is much else to which I might invite the reader's attention—the great storm, for instance, and the rescue of the lamb. I will be content to say, that—though a book of such humane matter and fine workmanship cannot be limited to any one class of reader—no one who wishes truly to know the lake district, and to understand what life there means, can afford to miss reading " Friends in Solitude." The wise visitor to that delectable country will take care to have this book in his luggage.

Lascelles Abercrombie

FRIENDS IN SOLITUDE

CHAPTER ONE: BY WAY OF INTRODUCTION, RECAPITULA-
TION, AND OTHER PEDESTRIAN MATTERS

The gladness of the heart is the life of a man,
And the joyfulness of man prolongeth his days.
ECCLESIASTICUS

Let us suck the sweetness of those affections and consuetudes that grow
near us. These old shoes are easy to the feet.
EMERSON

I

PERHAPS happiness that has stood the test of
time and of whatever comparisons subsequent
years of happiness have provided—happiness now
remembered in tranquillity—is as good a theme for
a book as any other. There are possessions found
in this world that were never lost, but only for a while
misplaced or overlaid; and when, in some hour of
determined search, they are safely recovered, I do not
see why one may not call together one's friends and
neighbours—those who are within call, and willing
—and bid them share the recovery and the delight.

It was Peter Dalethwaite, the old woodman and
companion of many years, who first suggested the
idea to my mind. It was only a suggestion, made
quite unconsciously, and would as likely as not never
have been realized but for Dalethwaite himself—the
figure of the man he was, the part he came to play

through ten of the happiest years of life, and the chance that, also unconsciously, he was destined to become, when the experiences he so largely shared were over, the most cherished memory of all they left behind. Our life from day to day, its difficulties, toils, pleasures, devotions, excitements, the great nature of the mountains, woods, and lake—he was in league with them all. And now, looking back, it is round the memory of him that these other tributary memories cluster.

Perhaps, were he alive, Dalethwaite would wonder to find himself woven into the tissue of a book. He lived and died a dalesman, known only in the narrow circle of the folk among whom he had lived for seventy years, and to them less known than respected and beloved; and that he should ever come to be talked about farther afield, and least of all brought bodily, as it were, into the public gaze, would have seemed to him an impossibility. He must have recognized the incidents and many of the conversations here set down, but the portrait of himself he would no more have accepted than the name under which it passes, and this, not because the portrait is counterfeit, but because its original was so constituted as to be totally incapable of regarding himself objectively. His characteristics, even his features I well believe, were as completely unknown to him as those of the ichthyosaurus, and enlightenment on them would certainly have caused more worrying of the accustomed and submissive lock of hair to which Dalethwaite's fingers were wont to travel whenever the peace of Dalethwaite's mind was suddenly broken, and perhaps a more than usually emphatic, " Well Aa nivver ! " in token of dismissal.

I have told elsewhere of the manner of our first meeting. He came as a protecting deity. Other men loving the woods as he did and jealous of their prescriptive claims, might have come with the pomp and ceremony of official or of self-appointed guardians: they might have shown diplomacy or bluster, and in either case challenged to combat. This ambassador played the rôle by divine right. The moment he broached the subject, I recognized that this tall bowed figure with the lank grey hair and clear-cut weathered features was the instrument of providence, the more impressive that it stood before me covered with human shyness and clothed in the working dress of a woodman.

The position was this. Disquieting news had come to his ears. He did not tell me, nor did I closely enquire, exactly what form the rumour had taken. It was enough that the woods he had so long shared with birds and squirrels, wind, sun, and rain were to be theirs no longer; that strangers were coming, perhaps to exercise formidable proprietary rights, presumptions, and tyrannies, to build a cottage cer-

tainly, and to establish by law a relationship with the
very sanctuary of the temple of which Dalethwaite
himself held guardianship only as a hired servant.
Strangers! To Dalethwaite, even when experience
of us had come to weigh in the other balance, the
name covered all the sins—scarlet, he held them, and
of too deep a dye to be included in the Gospel
promise—of summer visitors, of initialled trees and
torn branches, of broken bottles, banana skins, and
strewn paper. His cup was full. How long and
to what depth he had drunk of it I cannot say, but
he had at last come to the limit of human tolerance;
his stomach, with the trodden worm, had turned;
and this it was that precipitated our first meeting.

The business of pegging out the site of the cottage
had been finished an hour earlier. Had it swallowed
unnumbered hours or only minutes? I never knew.
The time it occupied might have been, at the backward glance, a portion of eternity rather than of time.

> For every wight that hath an hous to founde
> Ne renneth nought the werk for to beginne
> With rakel hond, but he wol byde a stounde,
> And sende his hertes lyne out fro with-inne
> Alderfirst his purpos for to winne—

And the experience now left me with a confused and
not unpleasant recollection of having grappled with
more fevered speculations than ever before in my life.
Like the fisherman's haul from deep seas, they came

in the number and variety of pure bewilderment, a hurtling gasping succession, whereof some were of familiar and expected type, others strange, and in some queer way stranger for being at once recognizable and very much in the order of things. And now, for good or ill, they were all encompassed and irretrievably fixed, as it were, within those few wooden stakes that stood a little uncouthly above the heather and trampled bracken. The task was over; the excitement of a purely self-interested purpose was fading into a quiet and almost impersonal satisfaction; and as I wandered along the margin of the lake, quick to the novel sights and experiences that emerged out of the mist and twilight at every step, I was in the mood for emotional adventure. All things worked together for good to anyone who should come to ask a sacrifice to the local deities. Thus came Dalethwaite. I could have given greatly.

II

He did not put me to the test. Whatever he had meditated asking, all he claimed was the preservation one and all of the Scotch firs, splendid and renowned fellows of giant proportions, massed irregularly between the promontory and the meadow that joined it to the mainland and the woods. Knowing Dalethwaite, as one day I came to know him, I can understand the treacherous seas his mind had voyaged through since he had first got wind of our coming. I should not be surprised to hear of disturbed nights. His apprehensions must have come in such crowds that the hours of daylight could not suffice to entertain them all. Besides, this crowd too has its late revellers. No more cakes and ale for them, verily; but they will have you awake to hear the chimes at midnight.

His concern for the firs was not based solely, as I then supposed, on aesthetic grounds. I learned the story later. It was an affair of life-long association, friendship, affection. As a mere toddler, nearly seventy years ago, he had come with his father to plant them. It was perhaps the farthest memory he could positively recall, though what he remembered was not so much the actual planting of the sapling fir as the thrill of a new adventure in a new world. It was the young dalesman's first introduction to the lake and the woods. The wise father, after satisfying parental obligations with a caution against falling into the water, had left the boy to his own devices; and the boy seems to have used wisely the freedom given to him. The work occupied many days, perhaps weeks—" for we may be cliver at our sums," said Dalethwaite, when speaking of the occasion, " but Aa don't knaw that figures help us ower much in calculating aboot childhood "—time enough, at any rate, to develop enterprise, and, after the first timid excursions, to launch him prosperously on to seas he was to voyage over till sunset and evening ſtar. He continued, I imagine, as he began, with little equipment, probably without chart or compass; the ports he touched at are unknown to geographers; the merchandise he trafficked in unsaleable in any markets of the world. He became in due time a woodman, lived and died a woodman; he would never have made or suspected his claim to any other title; but his main occupation, though he never knew it, was on the high seas of life, and of his ſtewardship there was only Peter Dalethwaite, the man, to show.

These trees, then, were his contemporaries, and associated it may be with his spiritual growth even more closely than his brief recital of the planting and his childish experience betokened. Perhaps in some vague and pregnant way he associated their ſtruggle upwards to this fine maturity with his own. Who knows but, for all his humility, he recognized in his own spiritual attainment something of the beauty, the perfection, the shapeliness of these firs that were the admiration of all who beheld them? I knew without his telling me of the hay-bay of the ſtorms they had buffeted, swayed and tossed under, defied; and here after seventy years they ſtood erect, splendid, trium-phant. Not all of them. What rank goes unthinned through seventy years? But I knew more vividly after his telling of the ſtory. In his language I caught the rush of many conflicts, the perils, the victories, defeats, apprehensions, paeans, and laments. For many indeed had been the battles, many the casualties. Some few had been uprooted in early years; the most had come to maturity, but of these one after another had fallen victims after longer or shorter intervals to some specially furious onslaught. At last the danger seemed to be over; the rank was now a rank of veterans, of seasoned campaigners. But the severest fight of all was yet to come. Every dalesman remembers the gale of the 'eighties. When Dalethwaite talked of it he told you how he came through the wrecked woods to the edge of the meadow, fear in his heart, to call the roll of his Scottish battalion. He still described the sight in the manner of one relating a tragedy, but ending on a note of triumph. "The heall woods, back and end of them, torn to bits, but only three of the Scotch blawn. Ey, mans! not blawn *doon* ayder. Just shaken at the roots and leaning ower into the oders' arms." He ended on the high note.

III

Dalethwaite had asked what was already given. While we thrashed out the portentous question his face changed as these fells change when the autumn mist that has clouded them at sunrise thins out and disappears. His very bearing as he strode away into the gloom was that of a man who had laid down a day-long burden, and was free. I was conscious of an immense satisfaction in the relief of this old man, this stranger, though the affording of it had cost me nothing. For not a branch of the Scotch fir was threatened, or even suspect. Indeed, our afternoon's task had been made easy by the natural conformity of the land, inasmuch as the site chosen was as clearly indicated by providence as it was agreeable, or least disagreeable, to Dalethwaite. On all sides from lake and meadow the promontory rose steeply, in fissured miniature cliffs, or up gentle slopes towards a plateau situated as nearly as possible towards its centre. At this point, in contrast to the hummocky heather-carpeted surface elsewhere, the ground was level and covered with short dense grass, over which some seven or eight sadly mutilated and stunted oak trees made a last brave stand. This area cleared would provide all the accommodation necessary.

It is true there were alternative suggestions. There are people in this world, not a few, who have this characteristic in common with birds of prey, that they are ever alert on poised wing, ready at a sign to swoop on quarry in suspected difficulty. They flocked about our heads, or fell like thunderbolts from the blue, at every stage of the proceedings. It was one of those well-meaning folk who begged us to leave the promontory entirely unbuilt on, and choose as a site the meadow that joined it to the mainland. There were a dozen cogent reasons in its favour—he traversed them all with a fine and impartial spontaneity—utilitarian, aesthetic, even merely Christian. We should avoid hurting the most sensitive susceptibilities, while we ourselves would share, in the undisturbed repose of one of the lake's most beautiful features, the common benefit, and I know not what added gain of self-righteousness. We could have a garden at our very door—geraniums in summer rows . . . parsley, a cabbage patch . . . all things pleasant about us, and homely, and hidden from the public eye. . . . It was a blazing August day. We stood awhile at the edge of the meadow, my friend declaiming the benefits this cornucopial scheme was to pour into our laps, I listening as one listens to running water that has murmured in one's ear a whole contented morning. The grass had recently been cut and harvested. We wandered over the browned parched surface, while an imagination more fertile than my own selected the site. The advantages were again set out in order of battle; repeated drillings had metamorphosed the raw recruits of an earlier hour into seasoned veterans, complete to the last gaiter button.

Meanwhile unnoticed clouds had gathered thick overhead. Our attention was first drawn to the changed sky by a crack of thunder far off, startling in its unexpectedness. The sound spread out over the surrounding fells, gathering volume as it bore down upon the quiet meadow where we were standing, and at last spent itself in the great empty space of the vale. Another followed, nearer and more menacing; the clouds blackened with amazing suddenness; heavy drops of rain were already falling. During the succeeding hour or more we had passed through all the experiences, short of immolation, of the roofless victims of a thunderstorm. By evening the rain had cleared away, the clouds cleared away, and in as fair and radiant an hour as ever ended a day of promise, we, my philosopher-friend and I, turned our steps towards the promontory. The call was overpowering. I was prepared to hear it all over again; to go once more through the order of battle rehearsed earlier in the day; to recognize the overwhelming odds against me—on paper; to realize opposition nugatory and morally bankrupt, if only I might see the place at the coloured end of such an evening. But there was no drilling—there were no troops to drill. The seasoned legion of the morning had gone; with the hosts of Pharaoh, it too had disappeared under the wave. Silent as stout Cortez and all his men we stood on the promontory looking across the meadow—the parched seared meadow we were trampling over when the thunderstorm broke— this site proffered by the gods for the domiciliary requirements of man. . . . It was already several inches under water, and the lake was still rising.

The submergence of the meadow was one of the tricks of the lake we had to grow to, and later anticipate and out-manœuvre by experiences. In the course of nine years we became familiar with the general run of them, but, as in the case of every great performer, a new one was likely to be sprung upon us, or an old one furbished up in guise strange enough to give it the surprise and discomfort of novelty. They were less tricks however than practical jokes. You might view them from a distance and enjoy all the tranquillity of a mere spectator. To live on the promontory was to share the practices as a victim. The triumph was to share also in their infinite mirth. It is a little disconcerting however, like the spiriting away of one's gold watch at the hands of a smiling conjuror, to suppose yourself the owner of some three or four statutory acres of land, and to find after a night of innocent rain that it is gradually shrinking before your eyes, until if the rain be persistent enough one of the four acres has disappeared, and the ground you walked over in pride of ownership but yesterday is now a portion of the bed of the lake, and has by feudal right become the property of the lord of the manor; to retire overnight a landsman, rooted in conviction, habit, and forthrightness, to awake next morning a sailor

22

marooned on an island with a passage of stormy lake between you and the necessaries of life.

Along one side of the meadow a causeway of rough local stone had been built, primarily for convenience in carting building material across from the mainland. It was not ill to look upon, but its rigid line, its rawness of stones newly quarried, its vague suggestion of a mechanical contrivance no longer serving a useful purpose, gave us increasing uneasiness. It was too blatantly an interloper that refused to settle comfortably in its fair environment. There was the question of the rising lake, but did it ever rise high enough to make the causeway necessary? Experience did not help to a decision, because that edge of the meadow sloped to a higher level than any part we had seen flooded.

IV

It was Dalethwaite who resolved our doubts.

Week after week of rainless weather had gone by. Summer was imperceptibly slipping into autumn. Here and there a single leaf of bracken had turned yellow, but the leafage of both woods and fells was still so green that this seemed rather a mischance than an indication of the changing season. The behaviour of Nature proved, a little startlingly, that even in her hands the keeping of beauty is not the sure thing one had supposed, for day by day a selvedge of slimy mud,

over which the reeds, once so beautiful above the
water, now sprawled in every posture of awkward-
ness and desuetude, widened round the margin of
the bay, its sun-baked surface hardening into ugly
frets and curves as the lake retreated, and suggesting
in its hue the refuse scourings of an industrial city.
Dalethwaite was attached to the word " nivver," but
I don't think he used it on any occasion merely as an
idle or effective word, or without fitting qualifications,
and he gave it as his opinion that the lake had never
been so low within living memory. Except for the
daily offence of the mud-flats, that spread their
tentacles like some immense squat diluvian creature
towards the retreating waters, nothing that all the
long summer gave was wanting to our enjoyment.
If we could no longer dive from the landing-stage
we could at least take the water from it at a flying
leap. Our bathing ceased to be an affair of numbered
or of ordered arrangement; we passed from water to
dry land and back again to water in the indifferent
way of amphibians, as the mood took us. Sometimes,
indeed, I caught myself looking towards the distant
fells with a sudden longing to exchange this idleness
and enervation for their fine ardours and endurances.
Once or twice, cooled by a recent bathe, I went so
far as to bring out map and tape-measure, and plan
with complete satisfaction a day's tramp. There it
ended. The fells were far off—heaven itself when

you reached them, but a wide stretch of purgatory
to pass through before attaining it. The choice,
even in the hard light of reason, offered no real
difficulty. If conscience troubled, clearly this life
in this rare summer was a convincing instance of
making hay while the sun shone, and we had an
adage to justify it.

Dalethwaite was standing on the farther shore of
the bay when I ran the canoe gently to land, hailed
him, and jumped out. He opened the conversation.

"Eh, mans! did you ivver knaw anything like
it?" In the dale, at whatever stage in the conversation, unless there is a substantive clear and convincing as the light of Ushant to guide one, " it " invariably refers to the weather generically, to the sun
specifically. Though in a season like this, and
Dalethwaite the speaker, and his gesture sweeping
in the whole beauty and radiance of the morning,
the grammatical vagueness made a moral certainty
only the more impressive.

"Yes," I answered, not unwilling to banter the
old man, " certainly I have, many times; though
from all accounts of the Cumberland climate I can
well believe that you haven't."

It was not the first time I had chaffed him—the
practice had grown insensibly with friendship—and,
serious though he was, I knew it could be indulged
to his pleasure. Nevertheless, the very slightest

shadow passed over his face, for his sense of humour was not apt to be the first weapon at hand when the affairs of the dale were under discussion. It was only momentary, and vanished in laughter, punctuated by mutterings of things felt but inexpressible. Then he turned his frank blue eyes straight on me, groped in one spacious pocket after another for his pipe, and began in due course rather sternly:

"Yes, naw doobt. It's a poor gimmerly sort of pleass, and none o' God's making, that hasn't got something good aboot it nows and thens."

This sally delivered he broke off, stuffed his pipe, containing the charred and dusty remnant of previous smokes, securely into the corner of his mouth, and began to fumble in other vast pockets for a match. It was his practice to keep matches loose, apparently indiscriminately as between many possible receptacles —though I am convinced there was always a box intact secreted somewhere on his person—and inasmuch as at no given time was he sure of their whereabouts, the search was generally a long and serious business. For the onlooker it was an affair teeming with quiet fun. The first assay would be made with an expression of complete and assured confidence. When, as was usually the case, it proved fruitless, and the most searching investigation ended in convinced failure, no word was spoken, but the bewildered look clearly indicated that the occurrence was unusual and must be numbered among the perversities of all this unintelligible world. The same process was then repeated in another pocket—a third —a fourth. Dalethwaite had now lost confidence. His mind was wandering in perplexities and surprise. Movements became a little inco-ordinated and purposeless. A flush mantled the bronze face. The rest was a feverish scramble to the four quarters of his clothing. . . . Compassion stepped in, and I produced a box of matches from my own pocket. He took his match—he took several, at my reassuring nod—like a defeated and still mystified victim of fate, and after prolonged effort got the fragment of tobacco safely alight.

" Anything more to say about the weather? " I asked.

" No yan's ivver done aboot the weather," he answered. " Aa think it's mebbe an act of Providence to give folk something to talk aboot and keep their tongues oot of mischief. Ha! Aa doobt if the dale mightn't as weel be deaf and dumb—except when it goes marketing—if it weren't for the weather. And why not? Did you ivver knaw anything more important or more ravell't? You may talk to your last breath but you nivver get to the back of it, and nivver will. Who'd hae thought of this? And now it's come, it's more wonderful ivvry day it stays. But not to ivvryone, mind you. Folk are aboot as mixed as weather, and naw wonder they don't always hit it off. Some of them growl and haver at it noo, and'll nivver be satisfied till rain comes and gives them something else to growl aboot. Grumbling's part of human nature, and it doesn't like to be kept ower lang to twanging the seamm string."

V

His pipe was out. Not the most noisy and determined efforts, latterly requisitioned at every third or fourth word, had produced in the first fine careless rapture more than, say, six clouds of smoke of volume and density at all commensurate with the display of energy, and these, though not the will to recapture them, had gradually dwindled as the monologue continued. As Falstaff's babbling of green fields was accepted as a sign by mine hostess, I had known very surely from the first there was but one way. It was always the same with Dalethwaite's reincineration. But this he never learned; in this he was impervious to the teachings of history, reason, and experience. He never knew his pipe was going out; he never knew it was out. He was still pulling with might and main though not a spark of encouragement had been given for the last two minutes.

I laughed at him outright. He looked questioningly. " I'm thinking," I said, " of the advice given in ambulance books on the treatment of drowning, never to give up artificial respiration until a doctor has pronounced life extinct."

He returned the pipe to his waistcoat pocket unemptied, to be used doubtless for another frustrate effort later in the day.

But he was disposed to continue the conversation, and we still talked of weather, looking out over the blue lake, and of wonderful seasons, and of many things meteorological and topographical. He told me of other late summers, of other low lakes, of the effects in the dale, on farm-lands, in the woods. For his part he had only one regret: he missed the birling of the becks; of all companionship he liked best the music, the glistening, the movement of swift waters, " the unremitting voice of mighty streams."

Before parting I broached the subject of the road. He gave me startling information. " You'll need it—ey, and more of it," he prophesied. " The lake's aboot as low noo as Aa've ivver knawn it. For high water you may add anoder ten feet likely, mebbe more. Aa've nivver measured, but Aa reckon there's a good ten or twelve feet atween highest and lowest."

" Why! " I exclaimed, " that will swamp the road and make us an island."

" Island? " he replied, " You? Aa don't knaw

29

aboot you, but it's sartin the headland will be. And
—yes—Aa guess you'll be in the same boat." He
was thoughtfully enjoying his own witticisms. "It
will be a boat for you, too, mind—or swimming."
Then, perhaps noticing a look of uneasiness on my
face, he went on: "Beſt raise your road anoder three
feet, and then Aa doobt it'll nivver be under water
more than a day or two in heavieſt flood. But, mans!
it'll be a grand bit of fun for the little lassie. Aa can
see her jumping and skipping like a new-born lamb
when she wakes up to find the water ivvrywhere
roond her, and she bewilder't to knaw where it
comes from. And it will be no girt ill for you nayder. You came to the headland for new experiences
—heall the dale could give "(this he said wickedly,
repeating a phrase I had used in a previous conversation)—" and this will be anoder of them. You'll be
oot of pocket too, unless the fun pays you. It'll be
boat back and to all day lang, for letters, milk,
ivvrything. You'll get a sight of experience afore
you've done. You'd nivver believe how 'tis—water
all roond you—land and sky, ivvrything water—
and the winds coming drooning doon from the fells
as though the wrath of God was in them. And this
island of yours ſtanding up ding-dong to face it oot.
It's grand, terrible grand! Aa've watched it many's
the time from this very pleass. Experiences?—you'll
get 'em here, thick! Look at it now—a bit of paradise.

30

Yan day as quiet as a sleeping baby, anoder the heall world in labour. . . . The great gale of this year was March—March going oot like a lion, as they say. It soonds well, but it was naw lion; it was sky and earth roaring themselves hoarse. . . . Bless you, ower in the sheltered dale they don't knaw what is going on here. They'll tell you as you walk alang, ' It's rayder slattery '—it's rayder yan thing or anoder. But doon here it's rayder nothing. It's the heall of it, and the biggeſt thing Aa knaw."

This effort had been interrupted by many pauses and encouraged by conſtant prompting on my part. The promptings were no longer necessary. He went on hurriedly, like a man who feels he has matters of moment to relate and muſt seize the words before they escape him:

" See! yonder headland was juſt a blur of smoke— you wondered it nivver moved. Same with the fells back of it. And not anoder thing could you see— naw fells t'oder side, naw Skiddaw, naw sky—nothing but black deluge and the wind screaming through it. Aa could but think of the old words, ' And the earth was without form, and void.' It was juſt that. They went backards and forards in my mind until, Aa tell you, Aa began hearing and seeing things more than a gale of wind and rain ower Derwent-water. . . . ' Without form, and void.' . . . And look at it noo."

Dalethwaite was transformed. I seemed to be in the presence of a prophet of old—a Jeremiah, an Amos, or other son of thunder—heralding a wrath to come. The discovery was surprising: a Pentecost. This silent man could talk to some purpose. It was a question of ventages, stops, the fitting moment. I had governed one of them unawares. As time went on either I gained in skill or he in adaptability. But this was a beginning. I had chanced too on a stop that gave the readiest and fullest response of them all. The storm-stop never failed.

I had pressed another that never failed of utterance, when, at the beginning of the conversation, I had asked Dalethwaite's opinion about leaving the five-barred gate that gave access to the road. It was not unsightly; indeed, at all times and in all places a rough-hewn craftsman-like gate is good to look on. I had a secret pleasure in this one. There was something reassuring about it. I could just descry its white bars gleaming through the sombre mass of Scotch fir when I went to the bedroom window on rising in the morning. The notion was of course a pure illusion, but it seemed to have kept things safe and snug over night, and, like a wedding-ring, to affirm the vow that all this was ours to have and to hold to death. It was true a neighbouring cottage pastured its cow in the farther meadow; but did the gate serve a genuinely utilitarian purpose? Above all, did it flaunt proprietorship too carelessly?

In the press of bigger matters, discussion of this question had been passed over. But Dalethwaite had not forgotten. Another stop had been pressed, quickest of all to respond, and the nearest instrument in quality to the ear-piercing fife of any in Dalethwaite's orchestra.

As I pushed the canoe from shore he called out:

" And that geatt—you'll want ivvry bar of it. Aa'd recommend three foot on that too, but Aa doobt twenty wouldn't keep them t'oder side. You haven't a notion of the folk that come speering and gleeping roond. Nothing's private to them. Fences, geatts, notice-boards—bless you, it's all the seamm value to them, and that's nothing. You'll find them yan day picnicking under your verra windows, and they'll so ootface you when you ask them to be off, you'll be perplexed to knaw if the place is yours or theirs."

And this also was truth.

It was an employment for his idle time which was not then idly spent.
SIR H. WOTTON

I

WHEN Dalethwaite, speaking of the cottage, had said: " It isn't ivvrybody's place, and ivvrybody wouldn't knaw what to do with it," there was in his voice a note of anxiety rather than of sententiousness. I fancy he was unconsciously expressing the verdict of the dale and not a reasoned conviction of his own; and yet he was close enough to his neighbours in spirit to share in some degree, however distant, the questionings that had occupied the dale since the first rumours of our coming had drifted in from the market town. A cottage at Abbots Bay! It was like a stone plunging in a still pool from an unseen hand. But whether from fear of straining its immemorial connotation or of hurting the new-comers' susceptibilities, or whether from mere zest of incorporating a new word into an immutable age-long vocabulary, the description of " cottage " was never used to our knowledge by anyone but Dalethwaite. Rumour whispered " bungalow," and " bungalow " it remained to the end. The usage brought unexpected rewards. It served as a touch-stone to the hidden things of dale life, an audible and articulate voice to dale taciturnity. From one mouth the word would slip plump and juicy, like a mellow pear—a gossip! Another would shape it with hesitation, timidity, as though in the performance of a desperate but necessary act—this we found more commonly in men, the silent men of the sheep-folds, and the high fells. Another—the humourist with few chances—with frank amusement, as who would say, " It's the rummest neamm ivver I heard, but if you maun have it, there 'tis! " And still another, with immense gusto. This kind would have you to understand that it had been familiar with the word from birth and with the people who used it by the grace of God to designate their homes of the latest style. It was rare in the dale, an interloper and unaccountable, and perhaps in more favourable soil a Pecksniff. Dalethwaite met it face to face on a memorable occasion in the person of the widow Brownlee.

The question was further complicated by the fact that the new-comers were strangers. What this term conveyed to Dalethwaite has been told in his own words at the end of the preceding chapter. To his neighbours it meant folk in smart holiday attire who rode to and fro in coaches, or who fostered a closer acquaintance as temporary guests, their well-lined pockets sufficient requital, their customs, no longer novel though still a trifle perplexing, pursued with business-like regularity, of setting out in a morning with waterproofs, alpine-stocks, and replenished knapsacks, returning at nightfall be-draggled, hungry, and exacting, and in due time taking wings, like the migrant bird, to southern homes—homes to the simple dalesman of unimaginable ease, convenience, and fineness. The acquaintanceship thus familiarized, in some cases justified of itself, in most sought and frankly tolerated through the pocket, could not be expected to prompt an enthusiastic welcome to new-comers who came, not as birds of passage, but as common and unprofitable settlers.

On The Point too! a cottage there! It was as though the Ark of the Covenant had been broken in the sight of the people.

When a crowd is suddenly shaken its feelings may ultimately be reducible to a common measure, but in the moment of disturbance it will speak with as many voices, tell the tale of as many faces, as there are men and women composing it. The individual is astonished into being himself. For this good reason, whatever bomb should have burst at his feet, Dalethwaite would never have been rushed into any emotion that was ungenerous or churlish, or into any expression of it that bespoke more than an interested or intelligent curiosity. If any words, it will be the woman's, that with her swift intuition and readier tongue gives the local habitation and the name to public opinion. Martha Hardknotts—

known to those who had the requisite courage, or to
the still fewer who laid claim to intimacy, as Mattie
—the voluble middle-aged wife of a lean, cadaverous,
fiddle-faced, iron-rimmed spectacled, silent man
named Job Hardknotts—had, as was her custom,
seized time by the forelock, and the dale was in
possession of her views, and inferentially of its own,
on the information brought by her silent spouse from
the neighbouring market-town a few hours earlier.
How Job ever came to impart the news is known only
to himself, or, more probably, only to his wife. He
was not a man who felt it incumbent on him to
break a silence however long and dreary, at any time,
or to disburse voluntarily, or at the call of conviviality,
information he might have acquired during the day
or any previous day. He was on the beaten road
what Threlkeld, the shepherd, was on the fells, a
Trappist by indestructible conviction. Incidentally a
carter by trade, God made him, and therefore let him
pass for a man. And yet there was stuff of true metal
in him too; perhaps literally—who knows?—" a
god though in the germ." As to appearance, of him
more than most it could be said I suspect, " When a'
was naked, he was for all the world like a forked-
radish," one bleached in a kindless soil. He was
silent, but as you shall hear he could speak fiery words
for a faith. When you take measure of Job Hardknotts you shall consider, perhaps ill-health, a life

37

of hard drudgery, a dour and crabbed disposition; God knows what of a birth and up-bringing. Also you shall produce Mrs. Hardknotts by his side. For " as the climbing up a sandy way is to the feet of the aged, so is a wife full of words to a quiet man."

Of the courtship of Job and his bride history tells nothing; even rumour is silent, for once humbled perhaps, and timorous, at the darkness of the mystery. Martha, the woman, discussed widely enough; Martha, the wife, never. The house of Hardknotts was shrouded in impenetrable mist. Or if glimpses of the life within were ever won, the dale was solid to a man in preserving secrecy. But it did know that in some errant moment the man divulged the news of Abbots Bay and the new-comers to the woman. The woman spread the news. Martha was not a gossip. Gossips are usually scatter-brain; human society has bred them as villadom has bred the sparrow. Martha could be silent, or speak with disconcerting brevity. Her forte was opinions, and she resorted to language, at least in public, for the sole purpose of expressing them. When I first mentioned her to Dalethwaite his only comment was the question: " So you've got to knaw her, have you? "—and the subject dropped automatically. But later I made a flank attack, worked round successfully to his rear, and, retreat cut off, he capitulated—in the frank, restrained, sufficient Dalethwaite fashion. "Oh, ay! Mattie! She's naw girt yam-merer, but she's terrible hard in the mooth—too hard a sight for mealy words. She's mebbe right, she's mebbe oftener wrang, but leastways you're nivver in doobt what she does mean. Her tongue cuts like a —no, not clean and done wid like a razor; but more like a pair of shears that trap from both sides afore they cut, and don't ivvry time get through, but nip, and at it ageann, wid a click-clicking in atween."

What Martha actually said on the subject, or one version of it—for besides being formidable, her tongue did service for a nimble and extensive wit—was told me very soon afterwards with frank enjoyment by a pleasant young woman who had occasion to seek Martha's cottage on a matter that quite naturally paved the way to conversation. She was not invited across the threshold—no one ever was. Hardknotts hospitality began and ended on the doorstep. The caller started a hare unawares by some casual reference to the news she herself had heard in the lane a few minutes earlier. She came of a house that neither sought nor spread news.

"Yis, girl, Aa knaw heall aboot it. Aa knawed aboot it lang sin. My man's naw slippery tongue, but mebbe he hears the mair in consequence. (Click, click.) He does na gaw trapesin' alangside his cart aw day and ivvry day withoot gettin' his bite in sometimes afore oder folk. An' sik a pleass too!

39

Aa wonder what folk'll be after doing next. (Click, click.) Whyivver folk in their right minds, if they muſt tak a holiday (Aa nivver needed oot o' t' sort myself), come gleepin' and speerin' roond the dales, Aa nivver knaw, shakin' their idleness like a dish-clout in yan's face. But to come an' ſtop when there's naething to keep 'em, an' naw ties of blood to draw 'em here—why, it passes a body to under-ſtand. An' sik a place too! Not a foot o' groond to graw a tatie in, whativver, an' naw roadd—what you may call a roadd—anywheres by; an' liftin' your face to the winder an' nivver seein' a body pass alang, year in, year oot. Liftin' your face indeed! (Click, click.) What would you be doing liftin' your face with naething but watter to look at, an' it naw good to anyone?"

Mrs. Hardknotts was well above the average height, gaunt, sallow complexioned, the dyspeptic hue of face being exaggerated to elfishness by crow's-feet so deeply trenched and puckered that the long insignificant nose in their midſt seemed nothing but a final gathering of them into one tightly knotted, smoothed bunch. The whole face sug-geſted a scaffolding rather than the finished work—monſtrously high cheek-bones, wide thin lips, as though engaged in a grim conflict of ſtrain and counter-ſtrain, a long, pointed, and indented chin. She was ugly, but it was an ugliness made im-

pressive and rather splendid by coal-black eyes,
piercing, and full of lustre—they had been beautiful
but for being placed so provokingly near together;
and glossy black hair parted with great distinctness
down the middle and drawn into severe loops over
the ears. Perhaps no face ever said more plainly,
" Beware! " After a momentary surprise the curious
observer might find himself questioning whether
such a face ever smiled, ever relaxed into any state
other than this. The further question, Could it?
seemed to provide the answer. Dalethwaite assured
me she had laughed more than once in his presence,
the occasion the folly or stupidity of a neighbour.
Oh yes, there was no denying to Martha Hardknotts
the machinery of laughter. And to her kind many
are the calls to set it going. She leaned over no
golden bar, this strange gaunt watchful sibyl, but
her station in space was remote enough to see this
earth, or her own narrow portion of it, spin like a
fretful midge, spin fecklessly. The woman herself
once envisaged, it was not difficult to picture her
leaning across the tides of day and night, peering
with those black steady eyes of hers. . . . And . . .
(I heard her laugh).

But there was something else. It was the face of
intelligence, honesty. At least, no nonsense about
her! When those jaws snapped, they snapped out
the truth, the Hardknott version of it, held with

conviction, fearlessly delivered on the instant. You knew, for instance, she was not the woman to thank you for a kind act, however kind, if there was " naw sense " in it. It was her constant phrase, betokening the acid test she applied to every word and deed. If you had talked to her of good intentions, instincts immature, purposes unsure, and the rest. . . . But I don't think anyone ever did, or dare—and doubtless a memorable addition to the precious Poyser collection was lost in consequence. A meeting between Martha Hardknotts and Rabbi Ben Ezra with a Boswell eavesdropping, would have completed it.

Long afterwards we were able to do Martha a service; there was sense in it, though not of her telling; she was in trouble, and she was in need, trifling as the service was. I suppose she came nearer to a smile than any of her neighbours had ever before seen. It was one of the most touching sights I ever beheld, as though some ancient fabric were suddenly convicted of scamped foundations, and had settled into a new position of momentary stability, its mistakes confessed and published, before toppling to the ground.

II

Another summer had slipped almost imperceptibly into autumn. The wealth of July foliage, green, opulent, and monotonous, was changed only in colour far into October, for the wild and spendthrift winds, usual in the earlier days of the month, had not yet come to squander it, except in the case of the chestnuts scattered sparsely among the plentiful oak, the first of all forest trees to take the autumn change and the first to weary of it. Their bare branches heightened the contrast, framing more remote vistas of colour, foretold too the inevitable end of the splendour round them, more secure than ever though it seemed in an air so quiet and so radiant. The morning was half gone before the last wisps of mist had thinned out and disappeared into the golden sunshine. The heavy dews, drenching my feet as I ran down the slope of bracken and heather for my morning dip, were woven at that hour into the tissue of innumerable cobwebs that spread in a continuous undulating veil, opaque and shimmering, from every spike of leaf and undergrowth; then, as the day wore on, gathered into single drops, clinging to gossamer threads no longer visible, till they too vanished. Only in the deep places of the woods did the dew remain and accumulate, filling the air between shadow and fitful light with the chill of October and the smell more native to the woods than all the vagrant odours of pine-trees or flowers, of earth enriched and unmolested since the beginning of time.

43

Such an autumn following upon a rather cold and unsettled summer is, of all the gifts of an English year, the most welcome. It is a generous apology for former misdeeds, it is an even more generous aid to the trials of the coming winter. Perhaps fullness of pleasure accounts for the special degree of exaggeration usual in the comments passed on every St. Luke's summer. It comes as a friend always desired, after an absence always too long, and we let ourselves go in the ardour of our welcome, in the satisfaction from day to day of a presence dear to us. Excess is the more easy because memory refuses correction; in the case of weather lets us down so badly. Whether any particular phase of it rouses us to gratitude or resentment, if the emotion stirs us deep enough we shall institute comparisons that sweep in, regardless of all truth, regardless of our own proved experience, the widest range of improbabilities. It was so now, in this fair smiling autumn. I had been assured over and over again that no such October had ever been experienced. In his gladness the passing wayfarer paused to add his own to the general verdict. I questioned pointedly, not so much because I was disinclined to believe, as to hold my dalesman on any subject in his more expansive moments. One or two were shaken on cross-examination; most of them, and the women without exception, stuck manfully to the heady word,

44

" Nivver! " watered down by the more wary to
" Nivver to the best of my memory." I began to
believe. I bethought me of the year before when
summer made an almost unbroken revel through six
months of it, splendidly young and joyous to the last.
But her end was sudden, a summary dismissal in
gales from the north-east that left a trail of white on
the fells. October when it came was well enough,
but to enjoy it one had to be swift of limb and to go
armed.

I consulted Dalethwaite, giving authorities where
I knew the names, quoting the phrase and its variations. He laughed, enjoying his amusement awhile
in silence. " Nivver? It's a big word, but with
some folk it tumbles oot of the mouth easier than
most little yans." After which comment on human
foibles, followed by a full minute of deep abstraction,
he named the year nine years back in which there
had been a similar October. This sort of subject
was to Dalethwaite as a match to a well-laid fire.
It burned slowly or swiftly, but it burned to the last
bit of fuel. He swept half the Octobers of a life-
time into his net, and sifted them. I expressed
wonder at his memory.

" Naw," he replied, " it isn't altogither memory.
It's trusting to memory, and not working it ower
much ayder, that makes folk so free with their
' nivvers.' "

And then he confessed to me that he kept, and had for thirty years or more kept, a diary, in which, at the end of the day, he jotted down any salient facts relating to the weather, and . . . I urged a full confession. I reeled out questions, half in jest, half in earnest, appropriate to the diarist of all ages. He was vastly amused. " Nows and thans," he said, " Aa've tried my hand at writing doon a thing or two, but it was naw good—like a child grabbing at soap-bubbles, except there was naw fun in it. The blawing of them was right enough, grawing bigger and bigger and floating off with the light in them, as though naething was easier than to put oot your tooa hands and hold them, roond as ivver, shape and colour and ivvrything. But when the grab came Aa found Aa'd nivver got hold of anything but the suds. You see," he added, " Aa didn't have any education, not worth calling education."

" If you had, Dalethwaite, there might have been no bubbles."

He went on to tell me that his note-books, in addition to comments on the weather, contained whatever he had remarked of interest during the day and a record of the work he had done. Some folk had a shelf of books to fall back on of a winter's evening, or a wife busy with her needlework and children yammering about the room. It was a grand thing to have something to occupy your mind, and Dalethwaite had his note-book, and back volumes to read over when there were not many fresh entries to be made. Spring, of course, was the great season of replenishment. " The heall earth waking up and buzzing aboot you like a hive of bees," he said. It was all a coming, and a welcoming—and wonderful. He noted the first greening of the larch, the first celandine, the first cuckoo, chiff-chaff, willow-wren, pied flycatcher, sand-piper; he kept count of all the nests, of the number of eggs, of the days of building, laying, hatching out; remarked the yield of leaf, flower, berry. " And at the ind o' the month a little sum in arithmetic gives me a pretty good notion of what's happen't, and Aa can set it alangside t'oder years. . . . Turning back's the wonder. You'd nivver believe what it brings you. It's like coming on a friend you'd clean forgotten aboot, thought dead lang since, mebbe, and finding him look as young as ivver; and you just sit doon and talk things ower. . . ."

III

There is, or used to be, a game called *That Reminds Me*, played of a winter's evening in homes where fireside games, mild, edifying, and Victorian, had or still have an innocent vogue. Each in turn, and with such readiness as he is capable of, names an object, place, or occasion awakened to memory by the suggestion of the previous speaker. It is surely

a game drawn from the commonest experience of
minds alone with their own thought or their own idle
fancies. It is of all others the game to play with
oneself; of all others the game of solitude. *Patience*
for those who will! Some there are who achieve
Patience, and practise it, God help them! religiously
as a Christian virtue when the other fripperies of the
day are over; others, alas and alas for lives in this
world dogged by suffering, weariness, loneliness,
have *Patience* thrust upon them. But as a mere aside
of the active life, even as the marching companion
of activity, toiling with you in your climbs, nimbly
stepping it ten strides to your one in the day's tramp,
and only tiring with you at the end of it, is there any
better amusement in solitude than *That Reminds Me*?
No preparations, no formalities; you don't invite;
it just comes. It may outstay its welcome; it may
come betimes when you would to God 'twere any
other visitor ; but that is when the heart is sad, yet
wants not companionship so much, and least of all to
be alone, as to forget.

I lay on my back in deep heather, busily occupied
with the game without knowing it. I had taken a
book at random from the shelves, and rowed over
to one of the farther headlands, where, in a little
cove close beside the water, I knew the whole day's
sunshine would be stored up. The book—I forget
its title, one by Father Tyrrell, of most excellent

fancy, since borrowed, and for the same good quality doubtless never returned—the book had engaged me for ten minutes, half an hour—I don't know how long. But the sun was still streaming into the cove, and the heather was warm and sweet-scented all about me, accommodating itself to every new posture as generously as a feather-bed. There was wind enough to give a gentle swaying motion to the blue water and to ripple its edges among the stones close beneath me, so close that I could roll over and let them play on my hand; but in my shelter I felt so little of it that the leaves of the open book now put negligently aside lay unruffled.

It was a place long known to me, one of the many hollows in the broken ground of the headland, but the only one that at this late season satisfied all the needs of idleness. The slope of its walls, its tussocks of cropped grass distributed over them, its yielding mattress of heather, provided comfort into whatever lazy attitude one chanced to fall. My head raised into the fresh position, I could see the long broken ridge of fells on either side of the dale, traced in firm outline against a cloudless sky, until far off they grew fainter and at last melted insensibly into the pallid green-hued mass that closed them in. This reminded me. There was scarcely a yard of the sky-line I had not tramped along, a good portion of it many times, and the vast circuit represented only a small portion of the walking and scrambling I had done. But two whole summers, a winter, a spring, and now a second autumn nearing its close! I was dismayed at the sudden impression of " the little done, the undone vast." The pressure of a voluntary, stupid, incredible deprivation weighed on me. I fell back on mental arithmetic, as though a non-swimmer should plunge into deep water for the consolation of catching at straws. My mathematical equipment, contemptible at all times, would not be risking disgrace from the fact that the quotient of such a sum could only be approximate at best; but it was near enough to accuracy to complete my discomfiture on the other count. However the figures were cajoled or whipt, they refused to allow that I had given more than an hour a week, nay, not an hour, of all my time to the fells. There was no gainsaying the fact. It assailed me in a defenceless moment, and brought pain, self-reproach, the chastisement of a squandered happiness. But the game was afoot—how swift its concatenations when one has it all to oneself! I was reminded and reminded, no longer seeking palliation for a wrong, but occupied solely with the thoughts hurrying through my mind.

The whole picture of our life at the cottage passed before me, its exigencies, penalties, exactions. I had lived them day after day, but they had slipped by unconsidered, until this moment the hidden price of its happiness. And now, not unpleasantly, I saw as in a radiograph, the sound rigid substantial skeleton underneath this life of our choosing, now tested to the full and found good. Incidentally my neglect of the fells was answered. I was perhaps no more master of my time than the man who is " something in the city." I had my correspondence—a copious one—my newspaper, bills, business affairs, to deal with. If a plumber was wanted, a carpenter, a butcher, or baker, I had three miles of water and wind to encounter, a mile of road at the other end, and the dawdlings and disappointments that are the pleasantries, or in some moods the pains, of commerce in a sequestered market town. If my own skill was equal to the requirements then I saved the journey, but probably lost heavily on the time and the result. Marketing alone involved the better part of two whole days in each week; the meeting and dispatch of visitors, since this also was done by boat, as much more time and labour as the capriciousness of the lake chose to exact. For the lake, as it was our chief source of pleasure, so was it our unending trial, even to bitterness; its moods, like a frenzied love, everything angelic, and betimes everything intransigent and impish. How often, at every season of the year, have we struggled for three hours of sweat and weariness to cover the less than three miles of water that perhaps a few hours earlier reflected every

line of our boat, so utterly calm it was; hugging the
shore, taking the shelter of each bay and headland,
for the little relief they might bring; every slackened
stroke a loss of precious progress! It was a grim
business, often to the limit of endurance; yet once
over, how splendid the sense of a fight to victory!
how good the rewards of a spread table, an afternoon
buried in a deep chair, a log fire generously fed, a
choice continually offered between sleep and one's
chosen book! But this too, this rest however well
earned, occupied a big portion of the working day
and must be reckoned a necessary call upon it. Our
market baskets, one on either arm, were accepted by
the market town with a smile of wonder, and I often
thought on tempestuous days with a smile of pity,
as the symbols of an incredible slavery. I fancy some
of our visitors, participating, shared the feeling.
But it was part of the life—the honest, wholesome,
fructifying portion of a life that might easily have
degenerated into the idlest lotus-eating.

And that easy chair, that choice between book and
sleep—they were indulgences soon and peremptorily
cut short. The post-office lay in the village two miles
away, and rarely an afternoon went by but some one
or two of the household must act beast of burden and
go laden with letters and parcels by a road too hilly
to bicycle with comfort. Letters and parcels were
the sinews of our life.

These were the big, protracted, routine employ-
ments. In purpose they corresponded with the
telephone calls, the giving of orders at the door, the
calling at shops round the corner, the whole effortless
and incidental procedure of well-regulated house-
holds, urban and suburban. They were a trial, at
their worst, only because they were enforced and
scheduled to time. Such offices as the hewing of
wood and drawing of water could be fitted in more
or less as we desired, and were counted in the order
of recreation—though, by courtesy only, the water-
pumping, a treadmill, convict sort of task, acceptable
only as a present necessity and in the promise of
state socialism one day distributing the burdens of
this world with an equal hand. In the act of pumping
I could have subscribed to the entire Marxian faith,
so this relief were provided. But the hewing of
wood, the whole process from the gathering of butts
and faggots to the shaping of them for use—there
I was an individualist, a " die-hard " sure of his faith,
his love. Almost I could have shed blood rather
than have any man interfere with my office as hewer
of wood. The very title, these long years afterwards,
sends racketing through my head the game that I was
playing more quietly that autumn afternoon in the
cove. " That reminds me—that reminds me," with
a swiftness that would be bewildering if sometimes a
memory, more fair to look on, did not hold up the

chase and stand fronting me while I linger over it, searching every feature, before it is hurried on. So there comes back to mind, as it came then, those mornings when we set off in the boat to gather wood, elders, children, and the dogs, these last including "Marcus," the Irish wolf-hound. How he came to have a Latin name I know not; but so was it written in his baptismal certificate, and recorded in the stud-book—and who, for an aesthetic whimsy, shall tamper with such authority? How more wonderfully we ever succeeded in packing so huge a creature, with two terriers, two children, and three, or on occasion four, adults into a boat registered to carry five, I have never comprehended. But the thing was done. It must be included among the wild, heedless, impossible deeds wrought the world over in merriment. Our boat run on to the shingle, we were soon scrambling over the woods like ants. Sure enough Dalethwaite would make an appearance sooner or later, and look on vastly amused, sometimes giving a hand when an unwieldy piece of timber had to be dragged to shore, but mostly content to direct the children to faggots strewn up and down the slopes, and to laugh at their efforts, successful and unsuccessful, ending in many a tumble. "Naw, not ants," he said when I named the simile—"not ants, nor bees nayder, though there's buzz enough. There's nothing else like it—just aw children together. Well, Aa nivver!"

The cargo was a work of patience, experience, skill, amazing even to Dalethwaite. The boat had to be floated in deep water, and the cargo conveyed across the intervening space by one or more of the crew standing knee-deep in it. We lifted and hauled, contrived ingeniously, swung aboard, steadied in position, to a landsman's chanty of laughter. No shifting cargoes on such a perilous voyage! On a former voyage, in days of our novitiate, we had experienced the bitterness and learned the lesson. It was the first time we had shipped an imposing cargo. The lake was roughened by a steady wind from the south-west. In rounding a promontory to gain shelter we ran into the trough of the wave, a big baulk of timber rolled to one side, the boat rolled with it, starboard gunwale to the water, and before righting herself had flung me sprawling among the nether timbers and deposited her cargo—the entire outcome of our morning's labours—overboard.

But even with this calamity in mind we continued our loadings to the last possible faggot, leaving only room for one rower on the bows seat. We shoved off, the gunwales almost submerged. The shore rang with cries of hail and farewell. A little apart stood Dalethwaite, shaking his head, his tall sombre figure, edging nearer and nearer along the ledges of rock, the last conspicuous object on land as we crawled round The Point. " Myjie," the boat of many uses, now pinnace, now tramp, "registered to carry five," her voyage accomplished, ran into home waters much as Birnam Wood did come to Dunsinane, and I believe Dalethwaite nursed a prophecy on the event every time it occurred.

Then the long unloading, the carrying up hill, the piling of the faggots, the stacking tent-wise of the baulks—these things all carried out with despatch during the afternoon, in readiness for the sawing and cleaving when the winter evenings came. And as memories, now I come to turn them over, to see them steadily and see them whole, I know not which I linger over more wistfully, those hours in the woods, the sunshine, the shadow, the laughter of children, or the wood yard in the dark evenings, with the wide door opening on to stars and gleaming waters, and within the scent of wood, the birling of the saw, and the lamp-light falling on the pile of freshly hewn logs.

IV

I was not seeking an excuse, good or bad, for my neglect of the fells. That came incidentally. My occupation in that idle hour was the game of reminiscence, the whole game, and nothing but the game. And once set going, on it went at a hop, skip, and jump into pastures new, fresh woods.

This rehearsal of the exactions, denials, difficulties of the cottage ran to an impressive total. The machinery was complicated. I had never before realized its intricacies, its calls constant and insistent on qualities not mine; on time, patience, devotion to which I gave no share; until those words slipped into my mind about parcels and letters being the sinews of our life. And now I thought, How smoothly and noiselessly it runs!—and again I was reminded of a host of dear, intimate things, almost too intimate to set down. I recalled, and Dalethwaite had remembered, the anniversary of our coming. He had remarked, though I did not take it at the time for anything more than a tag of conversation, on the comfortable way in which we had slipped into the cottage and the new life. He had foreseen troubles, annoyances. He knew nothing of shops, but he supposed folk like us were brought up on shops, that shops were the very breath of our being. He needed no workman the year round: we should be crying aloud for plumber, carpenter, greengrocer, all day, and it would be the voice of one crying in the wilderness. He conjured up a picture of accumulating worries, of helplessness, disgruntlement, disillusion, of hopes nipped in the bud. It grieved him. And when the time came nothing of the kind befell; and he knew it, and wondered. Through his eyes I too saw more clearly. I had accepted the achievement as one accepts a law of nature, the coming of day and night, the first primroses, and most other incredible perfect gifts. Now I began thinking on it. The silly fireside game was being played to some purpose by oneself quietly in this cove, where was no sound or movement except the lapping waters and the wind rustling the strewn leaves.

Yes, not a vestige of Dalethwaite's fears had been realized. We had slipped into our new home unnoticed, and the machinery of its life swung into proper motion at the very moment we crossed the threshold. So one reads of royal ceremonies, a button pressed, and weeks, months of labour and forethought suddenly coming to fruition. I had been, as it were, one of the onlookers, missing something of the wonder in my hold on past experiences, satisfied expectation, a preparedness not to be shaken into surprise or questioning. Trifles of the time now recurred to me. I remembered how within an hour or two of our arrival I had wanted some string. I remembered my blank stupefaction at the need for string, urgently; my shame in making the request. For reply, a bag of string of every length and thickness was given me. This was a peep at close quarters, verily, of

Hints of the proper craft, tricks of the tools' true play ;

here, too, the key to the innermost heart of the mystery. . . . I recalled other comments, acceptable and unregarded as Dalethwaite's, fallen from the lips of various guests. They had come expecting to

58

rough it. The novelty, the picturesqueness, the romance were to make amends for failures in creature comforts. There were no failures. There was a force at work from within, silent, tireless, irresistible. My game of *That Reminds Me* had brought me face to face with it. That little cove, warm and sheltered by the lake side, had become as a temple, and I was standing before the image enshrined there.

V

Such a calm and genial October—the month of storms—had drowsed us into a state of abandonment, of mistaken security. We were quite innocently practising infidelity to all the local deities, all save the matchless goddess now triumphing; our hearts turned against them, not in derision or contempt, but in sheer forgetfulness; and as yet our Hebrew prophet, Peter Dalethwaite, had spoken no warning of the wrath to come. We were free to go our way, speeded on every errand idle or serious with a blessing and a promise. At this distance of time it is impossible to say how the days were spent, or, to be more precise, how they spent themselves. I see them as it were in a luminous mist that half displays, half conceals, yet enshrines in its own brightness, multitudinous shapes in every attitude of dance, mirth, repose, languor. It is strange how imperfectly, even scrappily, the best-memoried among us can reconstruct a day, a single hour, of our past life. Who can give an ordered account of even its most eventful days? But in any case the landmarks of a prosperous journey are few and scattered; they stand forth between immense vacancies. It is sorrow, not gladness, that leaves its more sequent furrowed trail in the memory.

But I remember that the morning dip was continued all through the month, not a renegade among us. Youth was true to itself and jubilant, age forgot its dignity, forgot even its proprieties. The laughter and frolic that began on the long heather slope down to the water was soon to suffer a sea-change; though courage stand firm, there are flimsier qualities in the full man to fall victims to water at a temperature of forty-eight degrees Fahrenheit. But in the full man others step into the breach. The dive or spring over, we came to the surface protesting with gasping breath, boldly, a splendid reward of virtue. . . . The life of the day had begun.

One morning towards the end of the month when the preparations for marketing were going on, Dalethwaite suddenly appeared out of the wood, paused a moment as though uncertain of his next move, and then walked slowly across the meadow to the landing-stage, where I was hastening with all possible despatch the preparations for the voyage. The supercargo of children and dogs was engaged on its

own land affairs a little distance away, ready at a call
for embarkation. It was delicious to hear the ripple
washing against the boat riding at anchor, every
fifth wave falling with a sudden petulant boom on her
timbers; and to see her gaudy paint and bright
varnish, and all things business-like and handsome
about her, welcoming to a prosperous voyage.

I had thrown Dalethwaite a careless " good-
morning " as he approached, and continued at my
work without paying further heed to him. He
sidled closer; I felt he had picked his way among the
many obstacles awaiting shipment and was standing
motionless over me. If for no other reason I was too
curious to pretend further unconcern. I looked up.
He was gazing with childish wonderment on the
cargo, some of which was already aboard, the rest
scattered about where it had been shot down by the
casual dock-labourers, aged four years and eight
years, who were at the moment playing " ducks-
and-drakes " in the adjoining bay. To my look he
returned a " Well, Aa nivver! "—his customary
exclamation, like an embrace of all the emotions
appropriate to the occasion, as conceived in the heart
of Peter Dalethwaite. But they were too many on
this one to be so easily dealt with, and straightway
he broke into a loud opulent laugh, prolonged into
" Aa nivver! " abbreviated by sheer emptiness of
lung.

His laughter exposed a humorous side to the
business of embarkation that had never before struck
me. I stood on my dignity, but it seemed to me
very much like standing on my head, and I was very
soon laughing with him. I looked around. It
was funny—not in parts, but as a whole—like the
scourings of a jumble-sale, incongruous, unassorted,
ill-conditioned and well-conditioned, impeccable
and cast-off; rugs, coats, oilskins, oilcans, baskets,
kitchen utensils, a pair of boots, sundry wrappered
parcels, and a good-sized packing-case. The merriment at an end, he was concerned to know how we
contrived at the other end. " Gradeley ! " he rang
out, when the explanation had been given; and there
was no missing the note of approbation.

Then, with sailor-like scrutiny, he looked across
the lake, up at the sky, and back again at the lake,
coming towards us in hurrying blue ripples with the
light in them.

" Aa nivver go on the lake myself," he began,
" but if you have to market it's mebbe as good a way
as anoder, with sic a burden of things too. But "—
and he dropped into his serious manner, drawling out
the words with a burring emphasis—" hooivver
you're going to manage in wild weather? Aa don't
see much sign of change whativver; but it's boond
to come—fair autumn, foul winter—and to come the
stranger and langer, likely."

"Of course it will come," I assented, "but the rain'll make no difference. Look at our oilskins, sou'-we$t$ers, and the re$t$!"

"Rain?" he replied with an immense interrogation. "Rain? Oilskins?" It was a habit of Dalethwaite's to catch up the la$t$ word and to repeat it with a vehemence, almo$t$ a fierceness, that carried all the weight of the mo$t$ discreetly chosen expletive. That was the effect now. "Rain? Aa'm not thinking of rain. A sup of rain nivver hurt anybody—unless they'd made up their minds to it afworehand. It's the winds yarking and droosing the lake and your boat Aa'm thinking of; and a heall boat-load of oilskins won't help you to get through it. There'll be many a day when you'll nivver get roond yonder point, and many anoder when you'll get across swollen like a turkey-cock, and be reconcil't to coming back by road like a draggled hen."

"Dalethwaite, you're a regular Jeremiah."

"Jeremiah?" he muttered to himself. The name spirited him away. A bemused expression came over his face as though he were searching a di$t$ant horizon. I had seen it before, saw it many times hereafter. He went on in a lowered voice:

"Jeremiah! That's odd. A fiddle of yan $t$ring. Aa've nivver heard that name called since. Oald Slee—he was none so oald ayder, but Aa was a young$t$er, and to me he looked oald enough. He

63

was double-bass in our band. Forty years gone, ay, nearer fifty. Poor oald Slee! There was yan piece he would have ower and ower again—nivver tired of it. Aa don't remember what name it had, but we youngsters called it Slee's *Come Heamm Again*. Slee had a bit of a twirl all to himself, and then it was just a twanging of yan string, plop! plop! plop! betimes, the heall way through. Nothing to do but a bit of counting and jerking a thumb; the rest of him just a nodding head and a face of smiles. ' What shall we have next? ' we'd ask with a wink when a piece was over, and he'd wake up sudden, clearing his throat and fussing through his music, and oot it came—nivver let a chance slip. And yan evening Aa called him ' Jeremiah,' harping on his yan string, and sic a sight of pleasure in it; and the name stuck to the end. The oald chap must have been deadd near forty years—ay, aboot forty—and Aa've nivver heard the name spoken till noo. . . . Yan string. Mebbe Aa'm getting to the yan string time of life myself."

At this point the lady of the house joined us, accompanied by a dancing cavalcade of children and dogs. Her greeting brought Dalethwaite back from his voyage of memories. He responded in his courtly fashion, but I thought with more constraint than usual, as though he were shy at finding himself back again and the return witnessed by so large a company. But he was soon busied in helping us to get away.

Oh well, here it is: one gets, being old, at the sunset of life—which is the most beautiful hour of tones and reflections—a new idea of everything and of affection above all.

GEORGE SAND

I

ON the fells one forgets many things. We have toiled in the ascent, and the toil has been good, but we have carried with us our lowland baggage. The impressions we have received while yet we climbed and sweated and went scant of breath were only additions to the store with which we set out. But once over the crest our mind is washed clean of all past records, like a child's slate, and a new writing runs swiftly over it, leaving neither blank nor margin, for it needs no less a space than the utmost we can provide.

I had forgotten the dale far beneath me, now no longer in sight; I had forgotten it was Sunday. After the long ascent I had walked some way backward from the ridge and lay full length, looking into a cloudless sky. Suddenly the tolling of a bell reached me, at first so faint, so unexpected, I must strain my ears to make sure the sound was real and not merely one born of imagination, as befell Kinglake when a chime of village bells came to him on a Sabbath morning across the desert. It faded away into silence, returned, and came more clearly, but

65   E

no more convincingly; or just as I was becoming convinced, again vanished. By this time I was all tenseness and wonder. The silence of the fells was broken utterly by this sound so faint and far-off that I could not be sure of its being anything more than a trick, a whispering of my own fancy. After playing with the uncertainty some while longer, my curiosity at length became unbearable, and I retraced my steps to the nearest point at which I could look down into the valley, and listened. The dale, with its villages and its hot white road winding among meadows, knolls, and coppices, spread out beneath me. And now, while I leaned over the edge of rock, and was still wondering and perplexed, and half-amused, half-angry at my intentness on so trivial a matter when my hour's labour had brought so much else, a puff of wind blew into my face—and until that moment I had supposed the air motionless—and with it the sound came as close as if it were in a shell held to my ear. It was that of a single bell, its metallic harshness softened to the gentleness of an echo, calling the dale to worship. Like an echo too it seemed to come from nowhere, or to be a voice floating homelessly over the valley. But this was only for a moment, for looking a little more closely I was able to pick the church out from among the other buildings, standing apart, white-walled, in the midst of a green enclosure, in which stood groups of dark yew-trees and rows of stones, hardly discernible as stones at this distance, but so ordered in shape and line that they could only bear one meaning. These, as I gazed down on them half unconsciously, numbering the generations of dale-folk that had come and gone, seemed to give to the church and to the clanging bell a new and deeper significance, something that induced me without a moment's hesitation to leave the fells and to join the people, my neighbours, though few at this remote part of the dale known to me either by face or name, in their morning worship.

If the service began half an hour later, as I surmised, there would be time enough unless a direct descent encountered unforeseen difficulties. This it did. In many places where I could let myself down comfortably by clinging to rock or heather, the two terriers either would not or dare not follow without help. There was nothing for it but to wait patiently on their needs, though the occasion arose oftener than I could have anticipated, and involved more labour and more delay.

The bell was still tolling when I arrived. The dazzling light of an August morning was in my eyes as I crossed the threshold, giving me a mistaken impression of a gloomy interior peopled by dark motionless shadows. I stepped quietly into a seat just within the doorway, watching the various objects round me emerge into shape and character as my vision grew clearer. Never before had I been in a place of worship so utterly destitute of architectural or mural ornament; yet already, and increasingly as the service went on, I felt that neither had I ever before been in one, unless alone, so convincingly a house of prayer. The nave was without aisles, without columns, yet pleasant in its just proportions of length, width, and height. This last dimension extended into a steep-pitched roof, lightly timbered; its walls, pierced on either side by three narrow lancets, were hidden under plaster thin enough to reveal the inequalities of the Cumberland masonry, and showed the brushwork of the bluish whitewash covering it. This was the single decoration—this roughness and scouring of a surface for the light to play upon.

Stragglers were still coming in, the younger men chiefly, whom I had seen loitering by the gate, engaged, so far as I could judge, not so much in conversation as in the postponement to the last possible moment, like youth everywhere, of an enforced restraint. They came in one by one, moved uneasily to their seats, and after a momentary uncouth shuffling of feet merged unobtrusively into the quiet.

I wondered why these late-comers crowded every one into the back seats, when, so far as I could see, there were two rows or more in the front unoccupied.

The explanation came as I pondered it. The scrunch of hurrying feet on the shale path, and subdued whispers, though they did not appear to disturb the serenity of the congregation, struck unpleasantly on my ears and still more so into the mood I had so readily fallen upon. A moment later a group of folk of all ages, men, women, and children, filed through the doorway and down the aisle to the vacant seats. They were all clad, even the two little girls, in deep mourning.

It was their place on this one day, and the village had recognized their claim to it. Perhaps it was only my fancy, but from that moment it seemed to me as though all else were theirs—this building, the sunlight filtering through its narrow windows, the reverent silence of the congregation, the very quiet of the fells, the vague wandering outlines and dreamy colours of which filled the window-panes like stained glass. Even I, a stranger, come into their midst by chance, felt no longer either a stranger or an onlooker, but as made one with them by an acceptable offering.

In such an atmosphere, if thoughts flock into the mind more busily, they come more waywardly. For some reason for which I could assign no cause, they now travelled from the folk round me, not one of whom I knew by sight or by name, to the only acquaintance I had so far made in the village. I had never spoken to him, even his name and condition

were unknown to me. Our acquaintance had begun
one evening of early summer. I had been all day
on the fells, over Esk Hause, and round the girdle
of Bow Fell, and had just reached the stage of every
long travel in which weariness of limb will not be
put by for all our satisfaction in what we have done
or what we anticipate, when, half-way along the
village, I noticed in a row of curtained windows
flanking the road, one window where the curtains
were drawn far back, and the oldest figure of a man
I had ever seen—so it seemed to me—stood behind
it, his hands tremulously resting on some piece of
furniture, his head covered with a shock of snow-
white hair, tossed loosely in all directions, and like
his hands in continual palsied movement. The
moment he caught sight of me his face broke into
smiles, cheerful and welcoming as any wayfarer
could desire, the nodding head nodded more vigorously, and as I returned the greeting he raised a
hand and waved it, and went on waving it till I could
no longer see him. I had not passed through the
village more than three or four times since that day,
but on each of them I had reached it with pleasant
anticipations of my unknown acquaintance and of
his greeting; and always as I approached, the
window was just as I had first seen it, the curtains
drawn wide apart, and the old man who seemed never
to sit down and rest, standing there, smiling and

waving his hand as cheerily as ever. And again it was pleasant to remember that I should soon be passing his cottage on my way home. With this reflection my mind wandered back again to the little group sitting apart on the seats nearest the chancel.

The familiar service went on, and yet it was unfamiliar, and yet more familiar than ever before. It was both recovery and discovery, as though something I had experienced once and long ago, of which the intervening years had brought only an empty renewal, returned to me again on this morning and was nearer to the heart's desire than I remembered. It is possible that the hymns were a little less doggerel, the music less banal, the lessons more appropriate to the spirit of worship; but of these I recall nothing. That spirit was abroad, and these, whether in their own value good or bad, conformed to it.

At last the sermon. I knew, even before a word was spoken, that, like all else this morning, it would be an offering to the little group seated just below the pulpit; that however closely the rest of us shared it, the gift was theirs. Hardly was the text given out when a sudden vague apprehension came upon me. A name was mentioned—Luke Thornley—a reference to a life well spent, to years far beyond the allotted span, to a manhood that had been famous and was still remembered throughout the dales for its prowess in wrestling, and pole-jumping, and all

skill in the training of sheep-dogs, and to an old age
burdened with loneliness and suffering. Eighty-six
years of service were closed, said the preacher; and
because of their affection every man and every child
in the village would make and keep his own gathering
of the memories that long life had left them; but of
these only one mattered, for it was the symbol of all
the rest, the one most recently given to them, and
unforgetable—for who could now forget the picture
of that old man, who seemed never to rest his pain
and weariness, standing at his window with a smile
for everyone who passed by? . . .

I slipped quietly away before the rest of the congregation and hurried along the path to the corner
of the churchyard where I had tethered the dogs.
The temperature earlier in the morning had given
no indication of its present excesses. In this one
hour the surrounding fells had become ashen and
colourless like a scene in limelight. The air quivered
between contending furnaces of sun and earth. Even
more impressive than my own sudden experience was
the picture of the two panting slavering dogs
crowded together on the only patch of shade left for
them. In another moment they were leaping round
me as entirely forgetful of pressing bodily discomforts
as only dogs and some few human kind can be. The
greeting given and returned we set off along the
scorching road towards home.

II

" Dalethwaite, you were not at church on Sunday."
The old man's face was a study in confused
emotions. I had found him in the barn he had
appropriated within the last few years as a workshop
and a store room for stakes, poles, hurdles, and all
other of his handiwork. I had come abroad at this
hour chiefly on the dogs' account, but I had chosen
the woods rather than the fell-road on my own. The
woods could always be relied on to say most in the
shortest possible time, and on this August morning
they had the story of yesterday's storm to tell me.
And they were full of it. A dozen becks had sprung
into life, and went hurrying toward the lake along
the old worn channels or in new ones chosen in their
importunate haste, and so inadequate in many places
that their water had spilled over into neglected pools,
carpeted by tall grasses, moss, cow-wheat, woodruff,
and other greenery. In every direction I could see
blown trees, some prostrate but still clinging to great
baulks of earth, others, arrested in their fall, leaned
and swayed in supporting boughs. Branches big
and little were strewn over the ground thick as
apples in an orchard, or hung in mid-air torn and
twisted as the storm had left them. The vagaries of a
storm are without limit, apparently without law,
when they are given license in the woods. To follow
in its track is to find a new rendering, unexpectedly

73

sinister and devilish, of a phrase so seductive in its
more familiar use: the wind bloweth where it
listeth. It does, both when it is gentle and caressing
and when it is roused to fury. As I looked round I
could see, as I have seen a hundred times, that no
place deepest in the woods is deep enough to ensure
safety. It searches its victims like a sword plunged
hither and thither in the darkness, maiming or doing
to death as chance wills. I suppose soldiers—some
of them—find an immense grim satisfaction in con-
templating the havoc their instruments of war have
effected in the enemy ranks. There is always a
greatness and a wonder in the display of strength,
nowhere more potent than in the wreckage of forest
trees. But it visits alike the just and the unjust—
and then it is that our satisfaction, if we have felt it,
vanishes. The flower of our own ranks, as it were,
has also been cut down, and in the number some of
the cleanest limbed and comeliest, and some—friends.

Within an immeasurable space of time, Dalethwaite's face, so wonderfully wrought for play of
expression, had exhibited a wider range of emotions
than I had ever seen on a human countenance.
First, surprise; the soughing of the wind and his
own noisy employment had hidden the sound of
footsteps, and my shadow in the open doorway was
the first indication that a privacy he had every reason
to believe unassailable had been intruded upon. He

gave a visible start, and it was as though the abrupt
movement effected the next phase, so immediate was
it and so harmoniously disposed, like the falling
together into cheeriest designs of form and colour
when a kaleidoscope is shaken. The surprise did
not wholly vanish, but lost only its startled and
worried elements, and remained to quicken the new
expression of welcome. I in turn was surprised; I
had not seen a look of such genuine and abundant
pleasure on his face till that moment. Better than
discovering lost treasure is the finding treasure we
have desired and believed impossible, and more of it.
It was this I felt in a twinkling possessed of, and I
would willingly have had it rest there, but unfortun-
ately I had already blurted out that remark about
church. He was taken aback, the smile passed away
utterly, and a quick, searching, almost stern look
came into his face. At the same instant his body
swung to a rigid attitude and turned full towards
me, and I beheld the mild genial Dalethwaite in a
new light. I was frightened, as a menaced innocence
should be. My innocence was so complete that I
could not imagine an explanation. But the pinioning
was only momentary. Whether he or I smiled first
I don't know, but it was he spoke first.

"What were *you* doing there?" he asked with
great composure. I suggested that church was not
an unlikely place to be in on a Sunday.

"Not for moſt foalk," he replied, knitting his brows—"naw." Then perhaps realizing that the remark might be caſting an undeserved reflection, he added: "Church doors are wide enough for maiſt, as a hurdle's wide enough to let aw the sheep into yan fold. They may want a bit of coaxing or a bit of dreeving, but wid tham yan hurdle serves the heall flock." He paused, deep and serious in mien, and again went on: "Aa can't hold it the seamm wid church doors. Hooivver wide, some folk will find udders wider, and Aa'm of opinion a man should be grawn wise enough to make his own choice. There are these woods and fells. There is something bigger ſtill, Aa doobt—there's a man's own thoughts. . . . Only juſt afwore you came in Aa was thinking things aboot this old barn. Aa work here hour after hour aleann, but Aa find a sight mearr in it than sawing and shaping ſtakes."

He looked round, and then turning to me, he added:

"You've nivver been in it afwore, Aa believe. Isn't it gradely? The wind and rain singing roond, and yon blenk of meadow and trees through the door."

"What about the beck?" I asked. It was now swollen to a torrent, and its tumbling water could be heard above wind and rain, heard even while we talked.

"Yes," he said. "It nivver runs dry, ayder. Aa mayn't have the sermon, likely, but Aa've got the service and the music."

A long pause ensued. The last of the stakes was sawn, and the accumulation of his morning's work lay about the floor. The final stage was the pointing. Now, every stake has but two ends, and to the ordinary eye they are as nearly alike as two peas; it would seem therefore a matter of indifference which of them was chosen to take the point. To Dalethwaite the choice was one for deliberation. Each stake was subjected to careful scrutiny, tossed over and over in the hand, poised a moment and eyed from end to end, and in some cases the whole procedure gone through by a reverse process; till at length the momentous decision was made, and four or five swift dexterous strokes of the axe fashioned a point as regular as most of us achieve for our lead pencils.

In the lull of conversation I remembered that no explanation had yet been given of Dalethwaite's curious display of feeling earlier on. It came unexpectedly.

"Poor oald Luke!" he began. "Aa'd knawn him as lang as Aa'd knawn anything. Aa'd have liked to be there. . . ." He was curiously hesitating, turning the untrimmed stake in his hand backwards and forwards with the most aimless persistency.

" Aa started oot to go, and Aa'd got a good way forrard when Aa was stopped."

" Stopped? "

" Yes; Mrs. Brownlee. You'll not knaw her. She's a woman of property—came from Furness— a widow. Aa did ivvrything Aa could think to avoid her, but she'd seen me, and there she stood drawn up like a pillar of rock. Aa knawed my woman—Aa might have gone a mile back to look for something Aa'd nivver lost, and Aa should have foond her there when Aa returned. Aa hadn't a glimmer of what she wanted. But Aa needn't trouble aboot that— it had got to come."

" To come? What? "

" Whativver it was."

Dalethwaite paused. The pause was occupied in the same purposeless but more abstracted toying with the stake he still held in his hand, laid at intervals to the block, withdrawn again, and again scrutinized from end to end. A gleam of sunlight fell upon him from the open door. He turned in the direction it came, and my eyes followed his towards the sloping meadow with this sudden light across it, green and sparkling for a moment, and withdrawn as quickly into sombreness by passing storm-clouds. In the returning gloom I could see his face well enough to perceive that the remainder of the story, when it came, would show the narrator in a changed mood, summarily expressed in the resolute lifting of the axe and thrusting of the stake without further survey on to the block. Look and action were so formidable that I began to fear I might even at this stage be done out of the *dénouement*. I felt provoked, and jogged him perhaps a little impatiently.

" Well, Dalethwaite ? " I asked—" the Widow Brownlee ? She is still standing like a pillar of rock." He laughed.

" Hoo near had Aa got to her ? . . . It's naw matter. Aa hadn't got near enough on Sunday to say ' good-marnin',' when she drawed herself to the verra top and rasped oot: ' Mister Dalethwaite, you're nivver going to the House of God and to improving the deeath of Mister Thornley oot of mourning cloathes! ' "

" Good heavens! " I blurted out. " Did you shake her ? "

" Aa just stopped deadd," he replied abruptly. " She went on awhiles langer. Aa have a feeling that the space atween us was grawn less by the time she'd done, but Aa canna remember anoder word. Aa was worrit to find a word or two of my oan, but Aa found Aa'd nivver learnt anything that was of any use. . . . But Aa looked doon at my coat and trousers, and it came ower me that mebbe there was something in it. Aa'd clean forgotten aboot Sunday cloathes."

He looked utterly crestfallen.

" What did you do? " I asked.

" Aa turned roond and went quietly heamm."
Then brightening, and speaking in a more cheery
voice, while he began to slice away at the ſtake, he
continued:

" You nivver knawed Luke? "

I told him what I did know.

" That's right! That's Luke—you've got it! "
he exclaimed approvingly. " Many a yan knawed
him fifty years and knawed less. But Aa'm sorry
you nivver thought to go in for a chat. He'd have
sat doon for yance to reſt his poor oald legs. It
would have pleased him ivver so, and," he added,
looking ſtraight at me, and speaking with ſterner
voice, " something for you not to forget ayder.
You've telt me you wanted experiences of the dale—
you've missed yan of the beſt. God Almighty gave
no more care making the fells than making Luke.
Aa nivver went from them to him withoot knawing
Aa'd gone from yan of God's works to anoder."

" How long," I asked later, " had the old man
suffered so much? "

" Five years come the twenty-firſt of January.
Aa remember the day verra weel, ivvry hour of it."
And bit by bit, while Dalethwaite pointed his ſtakes
and carried them at intervals when a small bundle
had accumulated, to deposit on the ſtack at the far
end of the barn, patting the end of each one to a

level surface, I elicited the story, with many pauses and many promptings, of Luke Thornley.

III

Enthusiasm positively blazed in Dalethwaite's face when, in the only voluble portion of the narrative, he numbered old Luke's achievements: How he was here, there, and everywhere, at the beck and call of everyone, one night sitting up with a neighbour, another on the fells with the ewes and lambs, or just on some errand, day or night, that " likelier than not nobody knawed nothing aboot but himself "; how he lived alone, cooked his own food, tidied and scrubbed his cottage, looked after his garden, pigs, and fowls, washed his own clothes, washed every-thing—and washed everything thin, added Dale-thwaite smilingly—everything but the dimity cur-tains in the parlour—for them he must have skilled treatment. All this until his eightieth year.

" Well, he got word his only daughter was ill by Grasmere. He would go; he was to set off next morning at the first blenk. It was naw day for the fells, for a man nigh eighty. Snaw was on them, and more coming. Ivvrything wrang aboot it. A wind racing from nor'-west, in oot of the way corners a glisky bit of sky atween stacks of black cloud, gathering aw the time. Naw day for the fells; Aa knawed it and Luke knawed it. Aa foond him

buzzing roond like a bee. He was all packed ready——
the fire laid, pans of stew and porridge on the hob
to come heamm to. He was lontering ower lang,
going back ower things like a throstle wid its song,
and the heall of spring in front of it. He got away
aboot half-past seven. Aa watched them go, him
and his dog, Luke jigging alang like a fiddler at a
wedding, the dog, looking furder forrard, mebbe, and
just wagging his tail as slow and solemn as a grandfather clock. If they were garn into trouble Aa
knawed Mop was the best way oot of it. She and
Luke nivver apart. She was ill-farrant too——seemed
to have nothing of naw good left when Luke had
got his share . . .

" Aa went off to work wid as heavy a weight as
Aa'd carried lang sin. The wind was blawing and
drooning in the woods, and naws and thens a slatter
of snaw came wid it, and then glents of blue sky.
For a while it grawed darker, then it grawed a bit
lighter. Aa climbed to the road to look aboot. It
was terrible grand. A bank of cloud hid Skidder,
the wind shaking it oot like flax and dreeving lang
streamers up the lake. The dale——there was naw
dale, naething but the crag. But ower Armboth
there was a narrow streak of light, bright as an
orange, from nigh Bleaberry Fell to Green Combe,
and by my watch I reckoned Luke was up in that
light. It was aw make-believe. Aa hadn't reached

82

wood-end when it went oot like a blawn candle, and from Glaramara to Skidder there were naw fells, naw sky, naw nothing—just yan race of snaw and darkness."

" And the poor old chap was up in it? "

" It was ivvrywhere—Aa knawed it as well as Aa knaw my own hat—ivvrywhere! The more my thoughts the more of a havey-skavey they were, like a flock of sheep wid dogs after them. Aa knawed nothing till Aa reached the village, but Aa knawed something there aw at a jump. It was the hand of Providence touched me. Aa was garn head forrards when Aa heard a bit of a noise behint. Mans! it was Threlkelt. Aa'd nivver have heard him if he hadn't been getting ower a wall.

" He went for a flask of brandy, and we set off. Aa was sometimes of a mind to talk, to say anything to keep away from the ding-dang of snaw and the droon of the wind, but there was nothing to say, and a dree, lig-ma-lag-tongued fellow like Threlkelt wasn't the man to say it, and Aa needed aw my breath to keep alangside him.

" There were footprints the heall way up from Rosthet, and Aa got wondering aboot them, and who'd been backards and forrards, and when, and why, and ivvry other silly trantlement; but they were nigh smothered with the blawn snaw, and that telt me there'd be no tracks to help us furder up.

Dropping doon to the tarn they got thicker, and Aa saw Threlkelt looking hard at 'em. ' Jimmy! ' he said, maistly to himself. Aa only knawed what he meeant when we reached Watendlath and he went off withoot a word, poking his head in and oot of the byres, till Aa saw he'd foond something he wanted.

" It turned oot to be Jimmy, a big broad-chested man. The look of him made me feel a bit less lonely. Aa was glad when he came alang. He telt us he'd seen nothing of Luke, and that was aw the conversation there was.

" For the next hour, mebbe two hours, it was aw groping and stumbling, oot of yan drift into anoder, and a blanket of snaw wid the wind garn through it like a kennel of hoonds through bents. Aa can teall you nothing more aboot it, for it was the seamm ower and ower ageann. Aa got to feel it had naw beginning and naw end, nivver anything else in this life but snaw and wind.

" The change came sudden as the streak of a match—not the weather, mind, but my feelings. Aa was hard on Threlkelt's heels, or Aa'd nivver have heard what he said any more than 'twas a raven croaking. ' It's garn to come oot,' he said. 'Twas the langest speech Aa'd ivver knawn him make widoot provocation. Threlkelt's conversation is maistly a word at a time."

At this point in Dalethwaite's narrative another change had befallen quite as suddenly. In a twinkling of an eye Luke had gone, the snow gone. Once Dalethwaite caught sight of Threlkeld in a humorous light his eyes were dazzled to all else. He laughed, guffawed, playing a moment with his own concealed whimsy, and then added with a comic sententiousness:

" There are a moythering lot of dale weathers, you knaw. We all knaw them when we see them, but Threlkelt knaws befwore he sees them. Well," he went on, " Aa pulled myself together, but Aa could see nothing but snaw, snaw sky-deep, and hoo the sun was to come oot of it beat me. But Threlkelt had said it, and Aa didn't knaw why Aa shouldn't trust his word more than the snaw's."

" Was he right? " I asked.

" Yes—in time. 'Twasn't lang ayder, only seemed lang. Aa began to wonder if Aa could keep it up. Aa was mazed. Aa got watching Threlkelt's dog, lifting yan leg after anoder like a treadmill. 'Twas just that—a treadmill, on and on, and nivver anything but snaw at the end of it . . . "

" It was like waking from a dream," he continued abruptly after a long pause. " Aa felt as though Aa'd shaken myself, like Threlkelt's dog, and shaken off ivvrything, snaw and aw. It was Threlkelt's voice again—rapped oot like the crack of a gun, and

telt aboot as much to my ears. But the dog knawed,
and Aa knawed from the dog. Befwore you can
say it, he'd leapt forrard and stood wid yan paw oot
of the snaw, doddering from head to tail, and straining eyes and ears first to yan side and then t'oder.
Whativver was't? Aa didn't ask any questions, but
they were as thick aboot me as the snaw. Threlkelt
had started a conversation with his dog, what aboot
Aa was nivver telt. It just soonded a clatter of bones
to me, and the dog wasn't making much oot of it as
far as Aa could see, ayder—just garn a few feet
forrards, as though he'd picked oot a heartening
word, and then floondering back moythered and
snawed-up. Aa began wondering when the conversation was garn to take a turn. What came first,
Aa can't say—a sight of things happened afwore Aa
knawed yan from anoder. Threlkelt's grating and
clicking stopped. Aa thought mebbe he was winded.
'Tworn't that. He lifted his stick, telt the dog a
rough word or two, and aff it went. We followed.
Aa didn't rightly tak it in, but things were cooming
oot clearer ivvry moment. You began to see there
were craggs and hummocks and hollows afwore you
tumbled into them. The dog had ploughed oot of
sight; Threlkelt had done yammering—he wanted
aw his breath for scrambling on to some rocks—
there he was, going up hand ower hand like a cat.
Not a word, mind. Jimmy stopped. Aa stopped.

Whativver was he doing? Aa was nigh calling oot,
' Luke's nivver up there, man! ' when he suddenly
gave a whoop . . . "

Up to this point Dalethwaite had been carried
along buoyantly. That word " whoop " brought
him to a sudden standstill. I saw his lips quiver.
He was no longer the mere narrator, even though
of experiences his own. There are quicksands also
of memory, and Dalethwaite had fallen into one as
though unawares.

I waited a few moments, and then asked:
" Well? "

" Threlkelt knawed what he was doing," he
answered quietly. " He'd telt his dog to yammer,
and it set-to straight off, barking and yelping
as you could hear muffled echoes aw roond. Aa
noticed Threlkelt's head go doon listening. There
was naw need. Aa could hear it—clear, and nigh
as saft as a whisper of conscience. Two or three
quick short yapps came up from Blea Tarn way—
they seemed to come from t'oder side of aw the mist
and snaw that ivver was. ' Mop! ' Aa shouted—
' Mop! Thank God! ' . . .

" He was sleeping peaceful as a child. They'd
nivver have got near him, leastways nivver have
handled him, if Aa hadn't been there—not if they
hadn't done for Mop first.

" You knaw the rest."

87

*I am bewitched with the rogue's company. If the rascal have not
given me medicines to make me love him, I'll be hanged; it could not be
else; I have drunk medicines ... a plague upon you both!*
First part HENRY IV

I speak as it pleases God, and strive not for more eloquence.
DON QUIXOTE

I

"THERE'S Hardknotts of High Moss—Mister
Hardknotts most ivvryone calls him if they get
far enough. Aa always give him his Christian
name of Job—slip it in whenivver Aa can, like a bit
of grease, to help us alang together. You won't knaw
him, Aa doobt, a man with a feass and head oot of all
reckoning with the rest of him—the feass with no
more colour in it than a slowdy hankisher—lantern-
jawed and uncommon wide in the cheekbone, and
always wears, whativver he's at, roond iron-rimmed
speckets. (A laugh.) When you look into them you
don't see eyes ayder, as you'd think likely; you see
just gleams of brown light wallowing aboot like fish
in a pool. Then mebbe a twine of the head tells you
it is eyes after all, and they're coming straight at you.
He's a power in the pulpit, they say—preaches in
the oder dale, in a barn. Aa nivver heard him,
though Aa've knawn him ins and oots all my life.
Poor Job; he's had a sight of troubles—and maist

88

of them's nivver happened," he added deliberately, smiling at his own afterthought. "It's a disease that comes on a man and grips him till he's squeezed like a lemon. Aa've knawn both sorts, those that have had troubles and t' oders that have only figured them. Aa've knawn sorrow put years on a man, but Aa nivver knaw'd it make a squeezed lemon of him."

I didn't reply; I was busy with my own thoughts, and it was pleasant to let them take their way as lazily and silently as the little stream flowing between us, Dalethwaite on one side of its turf bank, I on the other. He bent down to it, lifted a handful of the sparkling water to his lips, rose and shook the drops free, and shouldering his spade and pick, went off without another word, as though I had not been there.

I had come upon him quite unexpectedly, no sound warning me of his presence before I pushed through a belt of dense undergrowth into the little glade where he was at work. His back was towards me, and this he was in the act of straightening by painful and difficult stages, in the manner of a man no longer young who has bent over his task too long. Hat, coat, and waistcoat had been discarded, his sleeves rolled to the elbow, his shirt unbuttoned at the neck, and collarless, disclosing an abrupt termination to the weathered hues of face and neck. This glade was Dalethwaite's favourite spot in all the woods, and he had been engaged there on the work he liked best, or so it seemed to me, and that not because he displayed greater zest or dispatched it with more alacrity, but rather for a contrary reason, that if ever he could be accused of dawdling it was just when he was occupied in this work of whatever kind in connection with the water-courses, becks, or runners, running through the wood. Other tasks he chose because they were due, or for some reason nakedly utilitarian; this one, without regard to season or necessity, because the mood was on him, and he had, like the schoolboy with his pennies, been saving up in defiance of how many temptations for the occasion to indulge it most prosperously.

In conversation, with a touch of exaggeration allowed to lovers, Scott confessed to the belief that he should die if he could not see the heather once a year. There are certain spirits—they are rare—to which such a love, I am very sure, is possible; and I believe Dalethwaite, if he could not have lived and worked among running waters would have lived a broken-hearted man. It was the running waters he rejoiced in, the waters that brought the tumultuous manners and the song they had learned on the fells down to the quiet woods.

The lake, except in storm, or on such days as we were now experiencing, when its surface faithfully reflected every colour and shape from its own fore-shore to the clouds overhead, counted less to him

than any feature of the landscape. And as for its
material pleasures, he set them at nought. It is true
he fished, and the manner of his fishing was such as
to make Izaak Walton turn in his grave. I have
watched him many a time of an evening when he
knew it not, I as desultorily engaged with my book
lying in the heather as he with his rod, hunched and
motionless as a heron among the rocks; till presently,
rod in hand, he would scramble into an adjoining
bay, pausing at intervals over some object that
attracted his notice, perhaps something in the woods,
when, abandoning the rod, he would disappear from
sight, returning in due time to find he had wholly
forgotten where it had been left; and I would watch
him with infinite amusement groping along the shore
on a search made increasingly difficult by the gathering darkness. And this was as near as he ever came
to the lake voluntarily.

It was in the becks he washed himself, from the
becks he drew his drinking water. I have come
upon him many times unperceived at both offices,
and looked on from a distance with the astonishment
and excitement of one watching a pagan rite or looking over the shoulder of a mediaeval mason working
on a gargoyle, so entirely lost to the world and so
engrossed in the wonder and refreshment of his
entertainment was the performer. The chosen site
was some channel where the water flowed most

merrily, or, better still, a basin of rocks worn by the
stream tumbling into it from higher ground; either,
so long as the light flashed in it and there was depth
enough to submerge face and forearms. Here,
bent low to the earth, he would begin quietly by
laying both arms in the pool, then suddenly straightening himself, lift on high handful after handful of its
contents, as the miser of fairy-tale is said to play
with his gold in secret, letting the drops trickle
through his fingers till at length the clenched fist
extruded the last of them before opening to replenish
it. This preliminary portion of the ritual over, and
resting his weight on both hands, he next buried
his face in the pool, sometimes keeping it there
motionless as long as a man's breath might serve, or
more usually raising and dipping it again so rapidly
and boisterously that one could hear and see the
splash of water swithered in every direction. Last
of all, if the day were hot, he would push his dripping
hands repeatedly through his hair, and, if the whole
series of evolutions had not at some inward call to
be gone over again, stand upright and shake his head
vigorously like a spaniel dog—like a dog, too, he had
taken copious gulps of water while splashing in it.

II

We had been talking together half an hour or
more in the beaten way of friendship, and at last

stepped boldly aside into bypaths of moral philosophy, when Dalethwaite made the final contribution recorded at the beginning of the chapter, and strode away with as little ceremony and delay as though I had not been there. It was abrupt, it was uncompromising, but it was as far as possible from affirming

> I am Sir Oracle
> And when I ope my mouth let no dog bark.

For Dalethwaite was wholly incapable of such an attitude even on moral questions. The discussion had been carried on at length, and though the fact of my seeing the world and life sadly awry that morning had been the occasion of it, I had recognized the truth and wisdom of all he said; I had yielded not only in the letter but in the spirit; we had laughed together, a running laughter; and now, as a fitting end, he had pointed his moral and adorned his tale.. What else to be said or done? Also perhaps it had suddenly occurred to the old woodman that this was his appointed day for the becks.

But, in truth, though I was still standing there and Dalethwaite had dived away into the trees, I had left him as suddenly and unceremoniously as he had left me. I had been spirited away at the mention of that name Job Hardknotts, and by the thumbnail picture Dalethwaite had drawn of him. Lantern-jawed, cadaverous, high in the cheek-bone, iron-rimmed spectacles — these salient characteristics, reinforced in the telling by an acid simile, a little surprising coming from Dalethwaite, convinced me that they could refer to one man only of all the wayfarers in the dale. He was without doubt the fellow that had left such a vivid impression on my mind at our first meeting; it had remained with me, as hauntingly as a silly tune that goes whisking through one's head uninvited and defiant; and two or three subsequent occasions on which we had met and passed had gathered round it a medley of fancies, curiosity, speculations that quickened the memory a hundredfold.

The man I had then remarked was seated on the front of one of the diminutive carts used on our hilly roads, a piece of rough sackcloth bunched over his shoulders and tied with string under the chin. His legs, partly because the sacking extended some way down them, partly because they were distorted into an incredibly small space, appeared to bear a similar relation to the rest of the figure that the penguin's flappers bear to the rest of the penguin. I had only gained this cursory impression of a lank bolt-upright body, an amplitude of sackcloth, and legs collapsed like a concertina, when the cart drove alongside and I called out a " Good morning! " loud enough to be heard above the creaking and rattling of the wheels. The greeting caused me instinctively to raise my eyes towards the man's face. Whether he made any acknowledgement, or whether a slight movement of the head was due to anything more than the jolting of the cart, I do not know. I should probably not have known had he volleyed a whole commentary on the weather at me, or had his face become wreathed in smiles, or had he done anything short of displaying a complete and unquestionable pair of legs. His face held me spellbound. It was the man's physiognomy that dominated all else, strange figure, strange posture, strange garment, strange everything. "Herbert Spencer," I thought. Nor will I now, after a closer acquaintance, go back on the resemblance; I would only qualify it by saying Herbert Spencer as Max Beerbohm would have portrayed him. Perhaps the big, round, iron-rimmed spectacles added something to the effect of a sovereign intellect, but it lay much more in the gaunt prominent features, in an immensity of chin and deep upper lip, in hollow cheeks surmounted by bastions of cheek-bone, and most of all by a steep-pitched forehead towering upward till, somewhere near the summit, it was lost in the recesses of the strangest headgear ever perpetrated for Christian uses.

This last article of clothing I was able to inspect at closer quarters later on, but when I had discovered that it consisted of some dingy woollen material, but whether woven or knitted I could never satisfy myself, I came to the end of all positive knowledge,

except that once winter set in it was capable of dis-
gorging two prodigious flaps that crossed under the
chin, served as "comforter" for throat and neck,
and were ultimately secured behind by a leather
boot-lace. Thus shrouded, the shape of head escaped
notice, so, too, did the monstrously long ears that
stood out almost at a right-angle, when one saw only
a haloed inventory of iron spectacles, nose, high-
boned cheeks, and thin colourless lips a little parted
midway, as though they were doomed to ejaculate
"Whew!" for ever more. To this must be added
that the complexion was deathly in its colourlessness.

But at that first meeting the cap or bonnet was
trussed up into an amorphous mass and pushed back
to show the full extent of the forehead. When afterwards I came to know of how voluminous a fabric it
was composed I gained some measure of the vastness
of the head on which, trussed however skilfully, it
could lie so lightly.

Below its edges, on either side and behind, pro-
truded a few long straight wisps of hair, hempen in
colour. Hair, similar in texture, but more tinged
with red, fell away from under the chin, like a goat's
beard; the rest of the face, cheeks and chin, were
clean-shaven. The expression of face was neither
stern nor benevolent, rather vacant, and as solemn,
impassive, and impenetrable as an owl's. Even
during conversation, and when the words, snapped

off into short lengths, hurriedly as though to be done
with them, travelled from mere commonplaces to
matters of moment, matters gay or serious—for in
our brief acquaintance we entertained both—nay,
though verily he laughed, if the word may be applied
to so uncouth and mirthless a sound, and the features
consented for a while to relax their confirmed habit,
they gave somehow the impression of working quite
independently of the man, Job Hardknotts, or of
other human agency, as though a spring had been
released, and the demonstration, timed, ordered,
regulated, must pass to its finish.

In this characteristic I read the pathos of Hardknotts' life. I came to like the fellow. At first,
between levity and awe, and all wonderment, I
pondered him as a curiosity, and, remembering the
profuse forehead and the dome surmounting it, with
hopes of high entertainment. So far I was repeating
the experience of Coleridge, who sat one day at his
tavern meal eagerly awaiting the words that should
fall from the lips of the stranger of noble countenance seated at an adjoining table. Time passed,
dish followed upon dish, and the god-like face main-
tained the expectation it raised in silence. In due
time apple-dumplings were served. The stranger
regarded them for a moment with ravishment, then
burst forth: " Them's the jockies for my money! "
and went mightily to work without further delay or

comment. Would a similar disappointment befall me? It did, and it didn't. Once I got to know Hardknotts, the promise of that lofty brow was forgotten, the intellect of the man became as nothing, for I had come to like the man himself.

But in my case the gods did not provide a talisman as readily as in the case of Coleridge. I had no dish of apple-dumplings to help me, and other means failed so persistently that I began to despair of finding them. But many opportunities occurred of remarking, that, in common with that other stranger of imposing mien, this man with the cart was capable under ordinary conditions of the most stubborn and protracted silence. I began to suspect he was dumb, and to pity him. How otherwise could the passing strange behaviour I noticed on two or three later occasions be accounted for? On each of them he was on foot, accompanied by a much younger, shorter man. Two horses and carts trailing heavily along the road were always to be seen somewhere in the vicinity of the two pedestrians, but the connection between them gave the impression of pure coincidence. The men might be described loosely as walking side by side; in reality the elder led, as it were obliquely, by some two or three feet; and this relationship seemed to be fixed and immutable as the stars in their courses. He at the rear was broad-shouldered and stubby, in gait singularly ungainly, splay-footed, clean-shaven, black-haired, and extravagantly red in complexion. Comeliness of face and figure is not indeed at any time the rule in the dale. There is a hard-featuredness, a gauntness, a tendency to a sallow and freckled skin, not usual in more southern counties; but these characteristics of a people, like the weathered thorn and fir, seem somehow to match their sterner and more sequestered life, and it matches still more closely their serious and sturdy spirit, their earnestness in all necessities, their independence of all fripperies. They are ill-favoured, and yet it is an ill-favour significant of big things; and it interests, and pleases, and grows more acceptable because of its rightness.

But this second man struck one in a different light. His plainness was emptiness. Eyes, nose, mouth, chin, the expression, the shape of head, all were negative. He occasioned no more interest and conveyed no more definite impression than a smudge of ink in a situation where one might be expected to find it. There might be surprises in him too, but in his case the question simply did not arise.

I had seen these two men together, and passed them by. The younger had returned my greeting by a screwing, rather than a nodding, of head on each occasion; of the elder's recognition I was still uncertain. But one morning, setting out for a day's tramp, I noticed them in the distance, and, swinging

along at my accustomed pace, I had soon arrived
within a few yards of them, when I slowed down to
their own leisurely pace. With this interval separat-
ing us we continued our journey along the dale for
another three miles. Not a single word was exchanged
between them; neither showed the least acknowledgement of the other's presence, nor did they
appear to be conscious of the beat of footsteps
following after. They were as men taking their
stand towards each other and towards the world on
the affirmation of another self-confessed misanthrope:
" O, touch me not;—I am not Stephano, but a
cramp."

Such were the two men and such the picture that.
Dalethwaite's casual reference called to my mind.
Acquaintance had gone no farther. The only
advance was this mention of a name, and it came with
greater import from the fact that I had already heard
rumours of Mrs. Hardknotts. But the man himself
and his strange fellowship had by this time become, as it were, familiar spirits. I had woven them
into story over the log fire of an evening. The
children's wonder had increased my own. They
drifted into conversation so often that we had to find
names for them. The elder we called *Aldiborontiphoscophornio*, the other *Rigdumfunidos*—not from
any suspected likeness to the originals of the names,
but because the names themselves, so rotund and

yet so remote from all terrestrial concerns, seemed of all human fancy could devise the most appropriate.

III

The quest of the two strange men (for it was no longer possible to think of the one without the other, even though the relationship were nothing else than substance and shadow) was delayed indefinitely after the talk with Dalethwaite—a fate that so usually befell any and every purpose in those days when it was not immediately concerned with the stark necessities of life. Except for these, and these lay gently upon us at most seasons, there never was a life I should suppose so little tethered by the rule, " so free we seem, so fettered fast we are." Or, to confess a paradox, the fetters we encouraged and yielded to were the fickle and wayward mood. If the day's meals were secure, or the pump had not given out, or we escaped other urgent misfortune, the day was ours. On looking back after many years, the long dream-like years from age to youth, the picture is too blurred to present a serious indictment, but I have the conviction that we sailed quite cheerfully, as an habitual experience, among the wreckage of argosies that we ourselves had commissioned, sent forth, and lightly abandoned to drift as the wind and tide served.

That morning of my coming on Dalethwaite surreptitiously added to the number, though in this case, as I shall tell, the ship (if I may keep a welcome metaphor) was ultimately reclaimed and survived many prosperous voyages before she ran into port for the last time. For while I wandered about the woods (and this itself was a betrayal of plans and promises) after his abrupt departure, half my thoughts were occupied with the lights and shadows, and the wonderful glistening of dew, and briars with monstrous red hips on them, and lichens tasseling the trees, and a robin that would keep breaking into brief wistful snatches of song, and a hundred other things; but the other half with the two strange men, and how I could inveigle the elder of them into acquaintanceship. Till at last I came out on to a mound, high above the wood, and saw the fells standing in the sunshine. Though a delicate haze hung over them, I could see right away to Great End and Allan Crags, every pike and brow and gulley, and long serrated lines of rock, and gentle slopes covered with grass and the autumn fern, bleaberry, and heather, those I knew by name and those known only to men like Threlkeld, who lived among them and had no other knowledge, except of sheep and sheep-dogs. I had tramped over them all. A gust of memories came upon me. I stood long looking, then retraced my steps hurriedly, not because I could the sooner execute my resolve, but because the resolve itself was running through my veins like quicksilver.

The wander-spirit often came over me suddenly,
uninvited and unexpected; and then my thoughts
and desires thronged together to one end, like the
swallows gathering on the barn-roof. It was not an
affair of day, month, or season. It might come on
such a morning as this, with sunshine and glittering
haze; but it came also when the fells were shrouded
in mist, and I succumbed as readily, though I knew
that the rain would drench me to the skin within
half an hour of setting forth. Indeed, I could never
make visitors believe the splendid fun these wet and
stormy days on the fells were. In the absence of
former experience, a little courage might be necessary
to make the start; but once at grips, once rebellious
hands and face were aglow with the battle, and
ears accustomed to the squish and ooze of boots
logged with water, the spirit threw off its last
encumbrances.

For whatever reason, it is those tramps in the mist
and the rain that I remember most clearly. Of the
others I retain the impression of beauty, of happiness,
of heat and toil, of the gamble with nightfall and
one's last ounce of strength for the vanquishment of
one more peak, of satisfaction at the last, and weariness—a sort of " twilight piece " in which the hues
fade imperceptibly one into another, and no outlines
are in any part of it strong enough to recall a memory
that should bring its own particular freightage,

whether of delight or travail. But as I look back on those days when the mist was over the fells, and again climb into it, I recall every stage of a brave adventure. The mist lifts, as it then lifted, and I have glimpses into a wonderland that had never been but for its secrecies; and when it closes about me once more, though I am led astray into many hazards and difficulties, the taste and feel of it are good in my mouth, like the sipping of an unsung vintageless country wine—I can even persuade myself it had an odour, more subtle but not less clean and invigorating, not less its own, than that of salt breezes—and at every moment I am all eagerness and impatience for the next scene, though what it will be or in which direction it will take place, I know not. To avoid danger I must watch my footing, scrutinize the little space between me and the unknown; but also I must keep a quick look-out behind and on either side if I am not to miss the unfolding of the curtain, and also the scene that is, it may be in the twinkling of an eye, revealed and obliterated. For the mountain mist is not a dead thing like the blackness of night; it drowses, or it sleeps soundly—it will lie sleeping a whole day, and many days, on some favourite summit; but when it wanders to other heights and descends into the valleys, its periods of rest are brief, its activities sudden, swift, and infinitely varied. It is the imp or magician of the elements. It will play pranks, and put you a girdle round the mountain as rapidly and mischievously as Puck, contrive the legerdemain of Prester John and the alchemies of Friar Bacon, and at last vanish, every shred and wisp, and leave you to bluer skies and sweeter, clearer airs than any morning of promise could have given, or, when the crest is reached, lie curled and motionless beneath you, more beautiful than ever in sleep.

I remember an occasion on which the mist did its worst—and its best. The experience was heightened by the fact that I was accompanied by a friend who had yet to be won from his deep-rooted suburban prejudices against any and all climatic conditions that did not come within the official descriptions " fair," or at worst " fair to showery." A good fellow withal, slow to anger, and to me chiefly remarkable in the sum of his excellences for his capacity to suffer fools gladly, of all tasks surely the most difficult.

It was by reason of this virtue that he agreed to set out with me and the dogs one August morning for a day's tramp. Rain was falling, and only the fells near at hand were visible. I had looked at the barometer, but not tapped it; my friend looked at and tapped it. But by this time lunch was in our pockets and the family waited at the door to see us off. Two hours later, when we had left the dale, we were climbing into dense mist, and the mist was a deluge. We had soon lost our bearings. The route, chosen a little perversely, was quite new to me. I had both maps and compass, but in such a drench, with a good eight or ten hours in front of us, it did not seem worth while to stop to consult them. Moreover, the wind blew half a gale, and was bitter cold. And this reminds me that there are mists and other mists—mists like those Tennyson saw creeping from pine to pine in the dale in Ida, that the lightest breeze will bear away and disperse like thistledown; and those others—and this was one of them—that stand up to the hurricane, pour forth their substance in torrents, and still stand unshaken.

The beck we had left some time back, in order to make a more rapid ascent, would serve as our best guide, and we decided to return to it. We walked in silence. I believe that I and the dogs alone could have seen the bright side; the spectacle of my companion, when I dared look back at him, and though he laughed, made me doubtful if it existed. The luncheon hour drew on, and passed. We were ascending more and more rapidly, keeping the beck, which had now become a mountain torrent, within hearing a little distance below us. I did not confess it, but what I felt to be a perplexity and a wrong, was, not the mist or rain, not the biting wind, but the total absence of shelter. Could we have seen a hundred feet round us we should probably have had choice enough. Our narrowed world was also a wilderness, destitute of every human necessity but rain—and Puck ruled over it. I had never before known his reign so villainous and so long unchallenged.

We found shelter at length, shelter the most complete we could have wished. It was no more than the rudest cave hollowed out of loose shaly rock, so low that we had difficulty in crawling through the opening, but once inside we found the roof rose a little higher at one end, and high enough to accommodate our bodies in a half-sitting, half-reclining posture; while the remainder of the space, carefully surveyed and after repeated attempts and repeated failures, at last proved sufficiently large to take our four legs and three perplexed and bedraggled dogs.

There we sat in great peace and contentment. We ate our sandwiches; the dogs, with each a parcel devised to his own requirements, crunched bones and biscuits. We smoked, and over our pipes fell to discussing our next movements. Again we consulted neither map nor compass, but by the time of day we found we had a free hour at our disposal, provided we returned by the same route, which seemed under the conditions the only practicable one. So we decided to go on, to take out our fullest measure of time, rain, and mist—they had already done their worst—and to reach home in the high mood known only to the tramper who has done his full day.

On emerging we noticed for the first time that the rain had diminished to a fine drizzle, the air was brighter, and our range of vision was more extensive. My companion frankly admitted the improvement, but to him mist was still mist, and as between one variety and another only a choice of abominations. I felt the evidences he had experienced were for him conclusive; and waited. I had not long to wait. I might have called out " Look! " earlier than I did but for the fear of raising false hopes, for not till the last moment does one know whether the spirit of mischief or the spirit of enchantment, or some unnamed and undetermined spirit, is in the ascendant.

There was scarce time to remark the signs, so swiftly they followed one another. This dripping, inky, impenetrable blanket that had hung close about us since morning was drawing farther away; it was whiter at every moment, a bluish whiteness, like a thin remnant of cloud when the storm passes; and its texture loosened, here and there fraying out into long wisps and streamers that floated away and disappeared. I had seen all these appearances before, seen the thinning, the blueness, the growing radiance, and often they had passed as rapidly as they came; and so a second time, and a third, and many times, it may be, the experience had been repeated, and in the end the mist had gathered again as thick as ever. So I watched and held my peace. My friend, too, was watching, and that I felt was enough for the present. And when the silence was broken I think no human agency could have prevented it or prompted any other than the words used. " Look! Look! " The cry went from us both simultaneously. We beheld a sight so wonderful, so sublime, so sudden, so mysterious, that neither mist, nor night, nor day had ever given me the like, or have ever since given. There, high aloft, so that we had to crane our necks to see it, hung a colossal shape, yet without shape, black, sinister, threatening. It seemed to be straight above us, poised like a hawk in air, but motionless. " What is it? " asked my companion. I didn't know. Or how should I guess at that moment, and standing in that presence?

I suppose it was a matter of seconds—it seemed an eternity. A trifle—no more than the floating wisps of mist we had noticed nearer at hand—resolved the mystery; for as the thin clouds of vapour passed across the great shapeless face, it grew shapely, towering from broad base to pointed summit; instead of the blackness, a warm umber hue spread over it; and the scars and fissures of unhewn rock seamed it; and it was enclosed, all save the base, which was still poised in mist, on a blue space, like a nimbus, that gradually spread farther and farther into vacancy. "The Langdales!" I said—"the Pike of Stickle!" The mystery had gone, but not the wonder, not the sublimity, nor the beauty. It grew more beautiful every moment as the mist cleared, and presently the whole fell stood forth in the sunshine.

And I turned to my companion and said: "There was a man once journeying on the road to Damascus, breathing out threatenings and slaughter; and, lo, a voice came to him from out of the air, and spoke, and he fell on his face and was converted."

Half an hour later we were on the summit of the Pike of Stickle, and the mist we had left lay below us like an evening cloud, and we tramped back over High Raise, over Ullscarf, down to Watendlath, where we had tea and hot cakes, down Ladder Brow, and home over the meadows.

IV

But I am not sure if the best part of those days on the fells was not the return at nightfall. At one point or other as one neared home, the whole day's perspective shifted, and all that had gone before seemed but a preparation for what was now coming. Long before leaving the wood I could see a twinkle of light, like a lonely star, then another; and these stars did verily dance together, appearing and disappearing among the trees. In some moods I was half-amused to notice a sense of displeasure at their waywardness, as though when they flashed a moment and disappeared I had been deluded by a promise that had passed away with them into the night. A little farther along, a bend in the road brought me within sight of the lake, and I could see the black gleaming water through the boles of trees sparsely scattered on the strips of land lying between, and a moment later the light flamed out, bright and steadfast, illumining the square of window in which it stood and stretching in a broad pathway towards me across the water. When I had come out of the wood I turned from the road and struck over the meadow, even though it was sodden with recent rains—for after a day on the fells one ceases to be troubled by such matters—and pushed through a clump of sweetgale in the midst of it, waist deep, bruising the sprays with my hands as I passed, though at that hour the air was already heavy with the fragrance. One familiar and trifling occurrence followed after another, but how impressive they became at that hour! And when I gave the accustomed shout, and renewed it again and again till the door of the cottage opened, and I could hear a tumult of answering calls, and see two fairy-like little figures racing down the path to meet me, and a third still standing within the glow of the porch—my voice, so clear and sudden in the deep stillness, awakening all that was dearest in life to an immediate and delighted response, seemed to me something outside myself, some power given me out of the night to command the utmost I desired.

V

I do not remember how long a time had elapsed in the desultory business of pursuing the two strange men when on a sudden full acquaintance was thrust upon me. I had been out for a long day with my bicycle. The toilsome stages of the journey were over, and now in the late afternoon I was trundling quietly homewards along one of the lanes leading towards the western side of the lake. Though spring was not yet, there was a softness in the air and a glow of colour in the coppices and hedgerows that beguile the waiting.

The ride had proved longer and more wearisome than I had foreseen. Drenching rain had added to the burden in the earlier hours of the journey, and now the wind, light though it was, blew direct against me, and the valley lanes were in many places covered with the deep sticky mud left by winter.

I knew the lane well, so well that in my present mood I do not suppose I should have given a thought to the situation if I had not suddenly, on rounding a corner, come upon two carts, one leisurely following the other, and both so far on their wrong side that I had difficulty in squeezing between them and a high

112

bank. When I was safely past I looked round to make a remonstrance to the men in charge, whom the carts had I supposed until then hidden from me. There were no men in charge. At this point he lane descended down a steep pitch, and I knew that at the bottom of the descent it turned sharply to the right, and immediately at the turn narrowed to cross a wooden bridge over a stream. But the looking round had upset my calculations; I had already got too far at the unchecked pace to take the curve; my bicycle skidded; and I was flung violently along the grassy surface to the very feet of—Aldiborontiphoscophornio! I had realized my destination even as I slithered through the mud. I remember the half-amusement, half-terror I felt at the prospect of colliding with him, and possibly knocking him over. Also I knew, though I had not yet seen him, that Rigdumfunidos was about three feet to the rear. . . .

All sense of time and space, all thought of all mundane affairs outside the yard of earth that bounded me and this man vanished. I was badly shaken, dazed, a welter of soreness, but of these I was for the moment hardly conscious. The first incident that struck me, and then sank dully into my confused thought was the approach of Rigdumfunidos. I do not know if I smiled or looked pleasant. I did not know till some time later that I was torn, bruised, and bleeding, and in considerable pain. My full

H

awakening to a sense of reality was the look of blank
astonishment on the face, now peering over me, like
a naturalist intent on a new specimen, of the man
before whose feet I lay prostrate. How long the
tableau would have continued I have no notion. The
end came with dramatic suddenness, the *deus ex
machina* Aldiborontiphoscophornio himself. I was
still prone in the mud when, to my utter bewilderment this strange gaunt iron-spectacled parchment-
faced figure, bending lower towards me, his eyes
rounded to the size and circle of his glasses, exclaimed
in a loud hollow voice, " You nivver knaw, you nivver
can teall! " threw his head far back, and with scarcely
a sound of laughter—though there could be no doubt
he perpetrated laughter—made the most monstrous
grimace I have ever seen on human face. It seemed
to be fixed there till the last trump; and readjustment,
when at last it came, was heralded by a long hiss, like
the rush of air in some distant cavern. Then the
features relaxed, the head bent forward, and once
more the figure stooped over me.

And now I regained my feet. That unearthly
display of grimace and laughter had revived me like a
douche of ice-cold water, and standing upright I
began to realize the extent of my injuries and
dilapidations. Some new pain started with every
movement, and for the nonce drew my thoughts from
the two men. I was making a rapid inventory of the

damage done to myself and my clothing. The survey engrossed me for the moment in the stupid intent sort of way usual after shock, till I was recalled to the situation by the sound of lumping footsteps. The younger man had gone to pick up my bicycle and was dragging it—it would not wheel—towards me. The sight of his grinning face and of my useless bicycle awakened me to a review of the whole episode—the plight I was now in, torn, bruised, and bleeding, far from home; these men's gross carelessness the cause of it; the callousness of that horrid laughter—or was it laughter? or merely a stereotyped expression that did service on all occasions of excessive emotion, grave or gay? I was in no mood to give Job Hardknotts (the fellow's own name for the first time flashed into mind) the benefit of the doubt, or to find conciliatoriness in the grin of his companion. I turned on him with anger upon my lips. Our eyes met.

" You're fair riddl't," he said.

" Yes," I answered savagely, " and——" My courage fell away like a garment, and I meekly added, " And my hand is bleeding pretty badly."

" That'll wash aff," he replied—" mud too. Yonder's plenty of watter," and he pointed to the stream a few feet away.

Even while he spoke his eyes had gone from me to my clothing. There lay the absorbing interest. He was voyaging strange seas of thought alone. I was become a mere spectator. Then, his scrutiny over, and lifting his face towards me, he opined:

" They'll tak lang stitching, Aa doobt——" He was going on. I felt convinced that at any moment he would tell me, " I nivver knawed," and with a gruff word of farewell I turned my back on him and limped down to the stream.

A Topic of this sort, of which the person himself may be considered as almost sole proprietor and patentee, is an estate for life, free from all encumbrances of wit, thought, or study ; you live upon it as a settled income. If you see a visionary of this class going along the street, you can tell as well what he is thinking of and will say next as the man who fancies himself a tea-pot or the Czar of Muscovy.

HAZLITT

God gave the whole world to man, and if he is left alone with it, it will make a clod of him at last; but to remedy that, God gave man a grave, and it redeems all, and makes an immortal spirit of him in the end.

HAWTHORNE

I

DALETHWAITE was almost as inveterate a wall-builder as Balbus. If Balbus surpassed him in sheer slavishness to the one occupation, or in skill, about which the voluminous records are curiously silent, it is a safe inference that the old woodman gained in the diversity of the many that fell to him. Ditching (though this seems a gross and malicious description, spite of all its pleasant south country associations, of the care and nurturing of mountain becks), felling, stake-cutting, wood-stacking, the making of fences, the building of dry walls— all came to Dalethwaite, and none ever came unwelcomed, unless juvenile mischievousness or adult vandalism had imposed the task. In what order of affection he held them, excepting always and all the work comprehended under "ditching," I never enquired—it would have been an affront to decency only a degree less idle and offensive than putting a parent to a similar catechism about his children. I watched, both known and unknown to him, and formed my own conclusions, but these shifted this way or that almost as often as the various occupations succeeded one another; and perhaps it was some measure of my growing affection for him that I did not wish to have them more stable.

But he worked with a difference; each office, according to its materials, tools, and environment, exalted one quality in the man and craftsman, and diminished another. Work on the becks and runners was in the main an affair of muscle and endurance, of steady slogging with spade and pick and bent back, and was only touched to its finer issues as it were incidentally, in the chance comment, in the contented face and leisurely progress, in some little act of orderliness, some trifling services of admiration, hope, or love, not reckoned in the labourer's hire; and perhaps most of all in the diversions related in the last chapter. In the felling of trees and in stake-cutting there was a greater skill required of hand and eye, but the scope for self-expression was more limited, the sequence more routine, regular, and rhythmical as clockwork; it was as if Dalethwaite himself became the perfect tool.

On this afternoon when I had come across him

unexpectedly, the light rapidly failing at the end of a day that had threatened rain from earliest hours, and was now beginning to carry out the threat in the "rayder slattery" fashion indicative of determination and abundance, he was repairing a lofty wall. It was the culminating stage of a large enterprise. He had made and fixed a substantial ladder with hand-rails to surmount the wall, and constructed a path several hundred feet in length, involving felling, bridge-building, and shoring-up, in order to give pedestrians a new route through a corner of the woods hitherto not readily accessible; and now he was replacing the few stones that had been dislodged.

It was this work that revealed the complete crafts-man. Your laying of dressed and mortared stone is but a " sad mechanic exercise," like Tennyson in a tired hour found the making of poetry. But in the dry wall every stone is a law unto itself, inveterate and inflexible always, often tantalizing, keeping patience and good humour at the stretch. It is the first parent, and still easily the most engaging, friend-liest, fruitfulest of all jig-saw puzzles; but whereas its latest offspring invites no more than idleness, and is a thing of naught, the dry wall is a craftsman's labour, is beautiful and enduring—the full measure of the craftsman's spirit—and makes unremitting demands on his vigilance, observation, trustiness, accuracy, and deftness. Yet a man may build, as an artist may paint, and carry on conversation. He stands back to study his work, shapes his lips to whistle or hum some air that trips to his mood, pauses to fill his pipe, surveys and looks serious, surveys again and smiles, toys with his material and his tools in a dozen various ways that are his alone—all the signs indicative of a man in tune with his work, and incidentally the pleasantest accompaniment to converse possible.

This opportunity of enjoying it had come unawares. It could only be brief. This was overtime by an hour or more, and the light was failing and a deluge imminent. But the first glance told me that Dalethwaite was certainly not oblivious of what the whole heavens were telling, but utterly indifferent to the message. He was going on till he could see no longer. He worked without the least sign of haste, in his usual deliberate fashion, which was not designed to compete with oncoming night or gathering storms; and at such a pace it was clear he could not finish it in the time remaining. But Dalethwaite was not going away till the last stone was in its place. I read the portents. When the light failed there would only be the top course left, and for that he would rely on touch.

I made a casual remark, intending to hasten on my way and leave him quietly to it. But he had noticed

something in my expression, for on resuming work
he asked:

"Well, what's tickling you noo?"

I gave him a brief account of my meeting with the
two strange men.

"Ay, that's Job, back and side," he laughed.
After a considerable pause in which he had selected
the largest stone on the pile and bedded it in position,
he continued:

"T'oder fellow Aa don't knaw, ayder him or his
neamm. Aa nivver thought particularly he'd have a
neamm—not for any difference it would make to him.
With Job it's anoder thing. He's a queer fish—oot
o' watter aw the time. Mind, he's a good man, not
a doobt of it. Aa've knawn him fifty years and mair,
and Aa knaw him aboot as well noo as the day we
started."

"He's one of the silent dalesmen," I suggested.

"Naw, 'tisn't that. He can talk hard and lang if
he's a mind to. He's mebbe a bit difficult to get
ageatt, but when he does, it's—or used to be, for our
talk has no more to it these days than a blenk of
summer lightning—it's like roosing a wasp's nest.
Hooivver you start, he works roond to sin and the
Day of Judgment. Ivvrything's grist to his mill,
and you knaw the grinding's going alang on a June
morning as sure as on a winter's night—you knaw
it though you nivver hear a soond; but when the

flour comes oot, sputtering and scattering, it's aw the same quality, whativver. Such a dust as nivver was! and it gets atween you and the sunshine—gets in your throat and chokes you."

This was Aldiborontiphoscophornio. History has taken some account of his chronological tree. It shows a respectable ambiguity, rooted in divers soils, flourishing in many climates, but ever yielding the same dead-sea fruit. Our branch of his day, prettily heavily laden it seems, fell across the path of Mr. Samuel Pepys. "His discourse being nothing but holy, and that impertinent," is the sufficient comment of Pepys. He adds, "I was weary of him." He would be. As an alternative to his "viallin" while pretty Mary Ashwell "danced above in my upper best chamber," there could be nothing for it but summary dismissal. It was otherwise with Dalethwaite. He had borne long and patiently. But Job Hardknotts came between him and the sunshine. It was a choice between a June morning and the Day of Judgment, and there was for Dalethwaite while this life lasted no doubt about the decision.

Dalethwaite had spoken with more warmth than I had ever known him display in a case in which his reflections were not wholly charitable, and recognizing this, a smile came into his face and he added quietly: "But Aa haven't a doobt he means well. It's likely more din than dow wid him."

" At any rate he has got a noble expanse of brow,"
I said, to give the discussion a lighter tone.

" Yes," he replied, and the smile ran into a laugh
—" it's got an uncommon big face to roof ower.
What else it covers, Aa don't knaw.   He's a puzzle in
the end. He's not a dale man, he came originally from
t'oder side Skidda . . ." There was a sudden pause; I
knew Dalethwaite muſt fill it; and when he did, rain,
and deepening gloom, and the slow weighted words,
and the deliberate movements backward and forward
from wall to ground, made an impressive fellowship.

" Aa'm afeart he's a sad life of it—lonely; and
more lonely wid aw the kangy talk and clatter that
goes ding-dong roond him. He's fouled his own
neſt, Aa guess. There's the woman at heamm, and
nothing but his own self aw the reſt of the time.
Folk who talk of nothing but sin and sorrow and the
Day of Judgment are likely to knaw a good lot of
them afwore they've done."

" Heaven but the vision of fulfill'd desire,
        And Hell the shadow from a soul on fire,"
I quoted. It was as pleasant to quote to Dalethwaite
as to bruise a sprig of thyme or sage in passing. He
had begun the top course, and was searching out
the shapes and inequalities of the ſtones he could
now only make certain of by the feel. The rain was
descending in sheets. With one hand reſting on the
wall he turned and faced me.

123

"Poetry ageann!" he said. "It's wonderful where you geatt it aw from. It had nivver come my way till you brought it. The sound's gradeley, but what comes ower me ivvry time is hoo it hits the nail on the headd."

"That's what poetry is, just that, Peter," I replied. "It gets home, and it sounds gradeley."

I stayed till Dalethwaite had placed the last stone.

II

Aldiborontiphoscophornio and Rigdumfunidos had become a legend, and though my few casual meetings with them during the next many months served to invest it with a quickened interest, they did little to promote the acquaintance. Summer came early and stayed long. If a meteorological record were put into my hand it is more than likely I should not recognize the description. Roughly, it came in May, flamed in June, waxed and waned in July, in August tried the tourist temper for some ten days, wearied of the sport, and, like the discreet beauty who throws aside her caprices and coquetries at the fitting moment, relapsed into a serene and sunny old age prolonged far on into October. Perhaps poetic justice demanded a peaceful end; but in fact the end came without warning, violently. I believe not even Dalethwaite was prepared for it. The last evening had given the promise of former evenings. During the night I heard a clap of thunder and the moaning of wind—" a wind that was all its own," as Boswell ventures in a moment of inspiration—but they were woven into my dreams and their meaning hidden. With morning the storm had broken. I ran down to my bathe alone, the rain descending in torrents, the ground strewn with autumn leaves, and the air full of the clatter of wind and water and swaying branches.

But memory brings a different picture, a picture of lotus-eating, of days that seemed endless as a child's day, of contentment in an idle round of bathing, boating, and afternoon picnicings in a favourite glade far down the shore, where we boiled our tea gipsy-fashion over a larch-wood fire, and played our games of rounders and ducks-and-drakes, or paddled barefoot among the rocks, or wandered deeper into the woods to gather flowers and, if he could be found, to have a crack with Dalethwaite.

Even so, my acquaintance with the two strange men had made some progress. They had recognized me when we again met. The greeting was not cordial, but it was unmistakable and it came readily, at least on the part of the elder man, who alone concerned me. At this stage progress hung fire, until one evening, returning from a day's tramp with a friend, we came suddenly upon them at a bend in the road a short distance before we reached our own turning.

There had been no warning, the carts were neither in sight nor hearing. The surprise, heightened by the fact that the hour was late and that we had not met or seen till that moment a living soul on the road, this, and some unconscious working of mind, perhaps too the sudden stark appearance of these two men like scapegoats leashed together in an unending, silent, spiritless companionship, hurried me out of hesitation and diffidence, and I stopped and boldly challenged conversation. I realized the desperate mood I was in when Hardknotts came to the halt of a man who has received a bullet, his companion three feet behind impelled by momentum to continue till he drew up alongside, and I experienced the relief of a complete and breathless relapse into the comic. It was too late to turn back. Besides, I was sufficiently master of my swiftly racing emotions to recognize that once the immediate look of surprise had gone from his face, it was replaced by an expression of friendliness and welcome.

We stayed chatting till the carts ambled up to us, and disappeared round the next bend. For aught we could see they seemed the last objects of concern or interest to the men. I cannot recall anything of the conversation, except that it went comfortably, that sin and the Day of Judgment played no part in it, and that Hardknotts assured me on two several occasions, with facial accompaniment, that " You

nivver knaw—you nivver can teall." He repeated
the phrase—so appropriate, in its unexpectedness and
strangeness, to the man himself, if so utterly inappro-
priate to anything said or implied—with such
immense physical effort, such a portentous display
of feeling and conviction, as to give the impression,
not of a fatuous habit merely, but of a solitary and
hard-won outlet for pent-up energies. It landed him
into absurdities, though they were none to him, as a
similar habit landed the Capuchin monk who showed
the sacred relics to Horace Walpole and had " got
into such a train of calling them the blessed this, and
the blessed that, that at last he showed us a bit of the
blessed fig-tree that Christ cursed." Such is the
nemesis awaiting a foolish habit, of which this of a
phrase constantly and inconsequently punctuating
conversation is among the most irritating and banal.
In Hardknotts' case its ghoulishness might have
excused it to the end. Besides, it seemed to me not
wholly irrelevant. Its iterated assurances, meaningless to him, called to something real and poignant in
my own consciousness, something that responded:
" Yes, but I do know and I can tell—more, far more,
than you guess, and it stirs me in your presence
rather to compassion than to laughter."

III

That was the first of what could be rightly described as our chats together. It was brief and perfunctory enough, but more propitious than I had expected. It showed that there was an avenue of approach, and that it lay open. Something more immediate had happened. I found that for me our nickname had fallen from him like an outworn cloak, to be exhibited only before the children, and handled a little more reverently, when we bartered old lamps of legend for new over the fire in the long evenings. The strange man was now plain Job Hardknotts.

Our meetings were frequent during the next twelve months. I knew in time the hour he was likely to be going along the dale; I knew more or less his destination on a particular day; and as the pace I walked at made it an easy matter to overtake or to leave him without demonstrativeness, and, especially when my company seemed increasingly welcome, I seized every possible occasion of developing the acquaintance.

I associate him with fresh sunny mornings, with the murmuring of the stream below us, with a road that curved and dipped from the shade of overhanging trees into broad spaces of meadow and wooded knolls, with all the gladness and confidence of the tramp setting forth on the day's adventure—

for these were the conditions under which I usually
saw him. He seems, now I begin to recall in words
and no longer in silence only, to fit uncomfortably
into the scene. It is young, joyous, infinitely friendly;
he, old, uncouth, solitary, forbidding. And yet I
never thought of him as out of harmony with his
surroundings; somehow he fitted into the large
generous comradeship of the fells; and as I look
back, the light that lay upon them, softening all their
irregularities and excrescences, surrounds him also,
and the strange ghoulish figure passes benignly into
its glow.

Sometimes we walked side by side the whole
distance from the bridge to Job's farthest calling-
place. He talked little, rarely or never reviving the
conversation when it lapsed, but contributing jerky
prods and flips quite contentedly while it was in
movement, after the fashion of the driver mechanic-
ally flicking his horse in the absence of more
enlivening diversion. On these terms human intercourse is a little disappointing. Perhaps I was
sustained by the sheer difficulty of the enterprise.
But always towering in the background, as it were,
was the vast uncharted head that had first attracted
my attention. It must yield something sometime—
more, at any rate, than these confirmatory nods and
ejaculations in a conversation limited to weather and
crops, horses, local topography, or any more trivial

subject that might be traversed impersonally. I began to feel satisfied that Dalethwaite's information was long out of date, and that sin and the Day of Judgment had become a spent volcano.

Then befell a day for ever memorable in my experience of the dale. It was a Saturday evening, fresh and beautiful after rain. I met Hardknotts in a lonely part of the road; to my surprise without either his cart or his usual companion. He was sauntering with slow halting step, his face to the ground. So deep was he in thought that he seemed quite unconscious of my approach until I greeted him.

At the sound of my voice he started back and gazed and blinked at me like an owl trapped in sunlight. My intention was to pass on. I felt that this was potentially the moment to which I had been long and patiently looking forward, that the mind behind that immense brow had been caught in the very act of gestation, and that here within my grasp, here possibly for the asking, was the living product. But it was too awful an occasion to seize. I was hastening on. But Hardknotts had stopped, and turned round. His expression, gesture, were confused, irresolute, almost painful. I drew up to him, impelled against my own convinced instincts. Before I could speak, he spoke. Hurriedly, abruptly, snapping out each word as though to be done with it, he spoke to such purpose that it was I now who was startled and confused. Diffident and hesitating as he had been a moment before, he was now upstanding and nonchalant as a highwayman, rapping out his question as it were a pistol at my head. . . . He asked —it was more like a demand—if I would not go to hear him preach—he preached in what he described as the House of the Lord every Sunday—he would be preaching there to-morrow. He spoke excitedly.

IV

I knew this " House of the Lord " well. It stood as the outpost of a straggling village some six or seven miles away, brick-walled, drab-porched, iron-roofed, its windows an abomination of white, yellow, and blue glass, shut off from a beautiful slope of bents and heather by iron palings—the neighbour in ugliness of spoil-banks, squalid sheds and yards, and a mill-chimney.

But I could face it all to hear this man preach. Yes, assuredly I would go—I would choose the first fine Sunday. He seemed relieved, quietened. It was pleasant to be leaving him in the most cheerful mood I had ever known him in, and to complete the state I asked lightly, as I moved away, what his text was for the morrow. It was like starting a train of gunpowder.

" ' O generation of vipers! ' " he shrieked back— and he meant it; he was combating a whole nest of

them. "'O generation of vipers!' Aa'll troonce
them, with their drinking, and cursing, and havver-
ing, and nivver giving a thought to the Day of
Wrath! He'll have them—oald Nick'll have them!"
His fingers opened and closed, as though he were
clutching one by one the perished souls of his congregation; his mouth sucked the dribble back through
its thin pallid lips, leaving a fleck of bubbles, stirred
and frothed by continual augmentation, at each
corner. The hollow, toneless voice rose again to a
shriek. A horrid demoniac vitality animated face
and gesture, like some long-disused engine of torment starting its ancient traffic afresh. The man
was transformed; he was become the prophet of
Wrath—more, the executioner. The dull sunken
eyes gleamed with fire, and seemed to protrude and
come nearer. I was perturbed, dismayed; but I
recollect the sense of relaxation that came to me
when I noticed two pinkish spots appear, one on
either crest of the prominent cheek-bone, and I
could find entertainment in watching them grow
brighter, and as they brightened spread a little
farther and a little farther, a duskier hue shading
away from the periphery, till the entire cheek was
suffused.

This relief given me, I could collect my thoughts.
I had fallen in with Job Hardknotts while he was
conning the morrow's sermon. The flood-gates had

opened so suddenly, the freed waters risen to such
an immediate torrent, because the storage was
already at the full, and his emotions fired to the
requisite pitch in the act of silent preparation.

He continued without pause, in a sort of frenzy,
the words tumbling over one another more and more
rapidly till in the end they became wellnigh inco-
herent.

" Many are ca'd, few chosen, Aa teall them. It's
a broad roadd, and they tak' it—goats! goats!
Thrutching and shouldering alang, the heall flock,
as if they were heading straight for bliss, and not
dreeving head forrard to perdition. Roose yourselves, Aa teall them, roose yourselves!—you're
drugged, you're wallering in sin! This life, what is
it?—a breath, a bubble, gall and wormwood, a thief
that comes in the night. A thief that breakks in
upon you, steals your souls, and carries them into
ooter darkness. Roose yourselves! Repent! The
jaws of Hell gape at your feet. It's the brimstone
light of it you teakk for the light of Heaven, and aw
it's good for is to glint your trantlements and your
sins, and put a dazzle into your een till you come
to the brink and topple ower. . . ."

He paused, as if newly aware of my presence.
The sudden silence and his fixed vacant gaze threw
me off my balance, and I put a question quite
involuntarily:

" Why vipers ? " I asked.

" Vipers ? " he replied, and off he went again, though more calmly. " Vipers ?—Snakes !—serpents ! It was the serpent that tumbl't Paradise doon like a hoose of cards. Eve did it—the Book tealls you so. And the serpent's twined roond the heart of man ivver since. Purge him oot, Aa teall them— there's no oder way. Jalap ! teakk it aw day and ivvry day—jalap—the Blood of the Lamb ! Purge him oot ! . . ."

Again he paused. Dalethwaite's words came to me—Dalethwaite himself came, not in the flesh, but not less healingly. I had put my foot unawares into the wasp's nest he had warned me of; but all the buzz and torment passed in his genial presence. I felt an immediate sense of peace and quiet. I was sufficiently self-possessed to hold out my hand—at which my strange companion seemed taken aback, thus giving me a further thrust into the light of common day—and bidding a hasty adieu I turned homewards.

V

I never went to hear Hardknotts preach after all. I intended to go, but one wet Sunday followed another, or if the day were fine my resolution oozed out drop by drop as the hour approached. Nor did I see him till many months later. The woods held me. Felling began in late October, and continued steadily though on a small scale far through the winter. Every tree demanded careful consideration; not one fell to the axe without a full enquiry, and until its own demerits or its injurious influence on neighbour trees were established to the point of certainty. I had Dalethwaite to appease as well as my own conscience.

The business of tree-felling went hand-in-glove with another enterprise. We had celebrated our Fifth of November since our first year at the cottage, at first humbly enough, but each succeeding year humility dwindled, till this year it found no place in either our preparations or our ambitions. The open meadow, lying between the lake and its fringe of Scotch firs on the one side and the woods on the other, provided an ideal setting for the display. For months past we had been collecting wood, sometimes of set purpose by boatloads, daily and in varying bulk by dragging some contribution or other behind us over the meadow whenever we returned home. The building of the bonfire was a serious affair, occupying a week or more of almost continuous labour, for Cumberland has its long and proud tradition in bonfires, and its faith is that on the building depends success or failure. We fitted and laid every branch, every butt-end, as faithfully as a good mason his stones. I know not how many tons of fuel, big and little, went to the making, how many knots of voyaging, how many miles of hauling and carrying, how much felling, chopping, and sawing, or how much laughter and fun; but when the day arrived, our edifice was declared by Dalethwaite to be well and truly constructed, had reached a height of nine feet, measured close on thirty in circumference, and was surmounted by a Guy Fawkes of colossal size, clad in a cast-off tarpaulin suit, hatless and bootless, as one caught red-handed in the act of secret villainy, towards which implication we had failed only in the portrayal of face, for try as we would we could neither cajole nor tease away a large half-witted smile, and the more we tried the broader the grin became—perhaps a Guy Fawkes' slavish tribute to the mood of his artificers.

The evening of such an anniversary comes slowly, but it came at last—a perfect night, blue and full of stars, for this hour without moon, and so still that the Chinese lanterns hung motionless from the trees. I had never supposed the village, or the entire dale, counted the number of men, women, and children that had gathered along the edge of the meadow, when, the busy preliminaries at an end and the fire started, I had time to share the onlookers' enjoyment. They had come from the four quarters, by boat, by vehicle, and on foot. Outward from the glare one looked upon a sea of white staring faces, and yet by a trick of light not so much faces as mere expressions, dismembered and disembodied, like the smile of the Cheshire Cat in *Alice in Wonderland*. The sound of many voices rose and fell with the flames, with the rockets, with the sudden startling behaviour of catherine wheels and jack-in-the-boxes.

For all of us, old and young, there were two or three hours of as splendid a crackling, swishing, roaring, and leaping of flame as was ever offered to Guy Fawkes, of glorious memory. Our own eight-foot impersonation of him had stuck to the larch-pole for about twenty minutes, relinquishing only tags and patches of its clothing at intervals till one foot fell off, and the other, and then the entire legs. The end came suddenly. There was a graceful stooping forward of both pole and figure, the latter for a moment simulating the attitude of the carved effigy of a ship's prow. A tremor went through it. A laugh here and there in the crowd only deepened the immense silence and expectancy. We had scarce time to notice the stoop, the tremor, anything, when Guy Fawkes, all that was left of him, careened into the night in an uprush of flames, smoke, and blazing débris.

This done, we let the children loose with squibs, rip-raps, and coloured lights. From distant corners of the meadow, from beneath the sombre plumes of Scotch fir, came for the next half-hour splashes of flame and sparks, running fires, racing shadows, and shrieks of laughter, the like of which this quiet corner of the world had almost certainly never before known. It was a scene of youthful frolic—it was nothing else to those who participated; but to those who watched there were other presences abroad.

The glare of the fire and the chasing lights over the meadow disturbed great shadows slumbering under the trees. One moment they were hidden in gloom, part and parcel of the night; the next they took shape, immense, fantastic, bodiless, and stole noiselessly forth, swiftly or slowly, swayed to and fro, lengthened, and withdrew again into the darkness. As the flames rose and sank in rapid alternation, so they came forward and retreated faster and faster, and in increasing number, till they seemed to be mimicking in ghostly fashion the mad-cap chase and merriment of the children. I know not how long I had looked on fascinated, when a voice at my side exclaimed: " Grand! Ivvrything!—grand!" It was Dalethwaite, his face bright in the glare, and as happy as if all the fun of the meadow were written on it.

Then he and I collected the strayed revellers, and gathering old and young we joined hands and danced round the fire singing " Auld Lang Syne."

VI

One morning towards the end of November a sudden impulse seized me to leave my letters, the

fireside, books, home, the felling—everything homely
and routine, and go off for a day's tramp. I had
gone some distance before I thought of the day and
its chances. The air was bitterly cold and penetrating, the sky heavily overcast. Skiddaw and all the
more distant fells were already lost in cloud, and
murk spread along the crests and was creeping in
places down the face of those nearer at hand—all
evil omens. I had not gone half a mile on the road
when the first pedestrians I had seen that morning
met and passed with the familiar, and in this hour
forlorn, greeting:

" Garn to brak doon."

" Ey, garn to be a mizzle, Aa doobt."

Indeed, a fine drizzle had already begun. Two
miles farther along it had strengthened to pelting
rain, and was increasingly interspersed with hail
and snow. To add to the discomfort the wind, from
one or other northerly quarter, had freshened, and
blew the sleet swift and hard about one's ears.

In the hope that it might prove nothing more than
a shower, I drew close up to an escarpment of rock
at the road side, so shaped and overhung with heather
and knotted roots as to provide complete shelter,
except for an occasional splash on my shoulder of
drops that accumulated in some crevice overhead.
To come by patience the more easily I lighted my
pipe. The dogs, at first too mystified to think of

shelter, at this call for endurance crept close up to my legs and lay down.

Some lumbering vehicle was approaching. It came round the bend a few yards away, and was followed immediately afterwards by another. I now knew what to expect, but the delay was longer than I expected, so long that a curious apprehension possessed me. At length the two men appeared. More comical figures, swathed in the garb hurriedly improvised against the weather, it would be impossible to conceive. The ludicrousness of the scene was obvious at a glance, but in the self-same moment I felt something restrain my laughter, something entirely vague and unrecognized, but not the less peremptory. Almost before the thought had taken shape, and under the same spontaneous impulse, I went towards them. As I approached, Hardknotts bent forward and drove both hands into his side, in the manner of a desperate effort to repress a paroxysm of coughing. The bowed, shapeless, shaken figure, in that pitiless drench of rain and snow and bitter wind, struck me as the most pathetic spectacle I had ever looked on.

The mere flicker of a smile came and went as he raised his head and found me standing beside him. The invariable pallor of face was more ashen, more death-like, the cheeks were sunken, and they and the lips were in constant agitation from pain and difficulty of breathing. On the prominent cheek-bones lay the same flush I had noticed at our last meeting, the same, but now so different, so sinister in its significance. He shook from head to foot. Except for the rough sacking thrown round his head and shoulders, his clothing was poor and miserably inadequate. Again the coughing began, again he stopped, bent lower and lower, and again pressed both hands forcibly to his side. A shock of memories came upon me. Our last meeting was within a few yards of this very spot. He was then the instrument of Wrath, exalted, fiery, triumphant. This same flush spread over the cadaverous cheeks was then the mark of the avenger, stiff-necked, implacable, without pity, committing his whole congregation to its doom. And now . . .

I turned and walked beside him until we came to the bridge, and there left him under a promise to go straight home and to bed.

VII

Work I could not leave kept me tied till many days afterwards; but I sought out Dalethwaite at the earliest opportunity in the hope of getting some news. Dalethwaite knew nothing; he was surprised at my enquiry. I explained, merely saying that I had met Job Hardknotts and he looked ill.

" He's nivver looked anything else all the years

Aa've knawn him," he answered. "And yet Aa nivver thought it was illness in his face ayder. It's likely the Day of Judgment. He's thought of it and talked of it till his face has grawn to it."

But when I went on to speak gravely, and to assure him the man was ill, and I feared seriously ill, he turned to me with a look expressive of both concern and self-reproach.

" Aa'm troubl't to hear aboot it," he said with great earnestness. "Aa always thought Job verra strang—nivver ailed anything that ivver Aa knawed of. But he's tramped aw the day lang wid that cart, in aw weathers, backards and forrards; and likely at his age he wasn't fit for the job—and we nivver knawed it. And wid aw his miles of tramping he nivver found a home at the end of it. Poor fellow! Aa'm troubl't. . . ."

*   *   *

Job Hardknotts had found a home at last. The next day I set out purposely to get news somehow, if need be to go the whole distance to his cottage, though it would mean my braving Martha Hardknotts. For some while I wandered on aimlessly, undecided whether to continue along the dale on the chance of meeting some neighbour or whether to retrace my steps and go direct to his house to enquire later. I had come to the last bend before the bridge when I noticed two carts coming leisurely down a slope in the far distance, their brakes full on and churning out the most dismal cacophany of shrieks and groans, such as only our dale carts, and of them only one or two neglected specimens, can emit. At the bridge I waited till they came up. As they got nearer I saw there was a man walking beside each horse, but I did not recognize either till the first one, a complete stranger, had gone by. The second proved to be him whom we had always known and described as " the other man " or, more respectfully, as Rigdumfunidos. He made as though he were going to pass on, not churlishly, but simply vacuously. I stopped him. At that moment it occurred to me that I had never yet heard his voice.

" How is Hardknotts? " I asked.

" He's put doon," he answered.

" He's what? "

" He's put doon . . . deadd. . . . A week come Saturday."

Aldiborontiphoscophornio had gone, and Rigdumfunidos spoken the first and last words I ever heard him speak.

The sky was come upon the earth at last,
Sifting thinly down as endlessly
As though within the system of blind planets
Something had been forgot or overdriven.

GORDON BOTTOMLEY

I

ABOUT this time there occurred an incident from which I date, not the birthday of Dalethwaite's friendship—for that had begun shyly and tentatively from the first, like the life working its will underground—but perhaps rather its coming of age. Men are not accustomed, as many women are, to swear eternal friendship. By nature more sensitive and more reserved under their ancestral coat of mail, and however careless and indifferent a show it is made to assume, they are instinctively shy of exposing the intimacies that lie beneath, either from a fear of ridicule or disdain, or—a less questionable merit— from a warning prudence against a possible fallibility, insecurity, delusion. But men are not necessarily less aware when the fateful hour has arrived. In this case I had been willing enough to hasten it, but Peter, never in a hurry at any time, was of all men least likely to break his rule in a matter that demanded caution in lesser natures. He was leisurely in all things, this man of the clear eye, low voice, and limber stride—in felling a tree, in building a

wall, in casting a fly, in speech, in the processes of
thought, and all these he had practised year in and
year out, and mastered them—how should he hasten
over friendship of which in his lonely hidden life
he had known so little? One night we met by a
strange accident, and the thing was done.

All this while I had known Dalethwaite's cottage
only from a distance, lying remote from the coach-
road on a hillside of grass, heather, and bracken, that
both in situation and character served most fittingly
to connect the pastoral valley and its grey clustered
hamlet with the sombre mass overhead. If in glacial
ages a boulder had once started on its course downwards in this direction it would probably have come
to rest in this identical place. Thus situated the
cottage was sheltered from the weight of the fiercest
gales, those from the south-west, but to all the gentler
elements it lay as completely open as though designed
with the sole purpose of inviting them. Its whitewashed walls, its elevation above the road, its background of frowning hill, made it a conspicuous object
to all wayfarers, whether they were descending from
the fells or tramping by road, and, as I have heard
shepherds tell, oftentimes a most welcome one.

I had of late been chaffing Dalethwaite about it,
called it " morning star " and " evening star " by
turns, with a reference to another cottage and another
dalesman, by name " Michael," away over our

eastern fells, and long ago; and laughingly assured him that the designations could be given to his cottage only by courtesy, since it was more a warning than a welcome. He was puzzled to know my meaning. I chose to give the one that conveyed no hint. When I did go as visitor I had at last determined it should be by invitation, unsolicited and frankly convincing. I was soon to know how far otherwise the gods had schemed things. I put Dalethwaite off with general comments on inaccessibility, remoteness from the road, the nature of the track between road and cottage, leading doubtfully anywhere, inviting nowhere. The answer was satisfactory enough to produce a laugh.

" Aa'm aleann," he said, " and what pleass could you have better for a lonely man ? "

In the pause that followed, and still eyeing me a little uneasily, perhaps there arose in his mind the contrast between my suggested picture of hospitality and his own of selfishness, thus withdrawn from the cottages and peoples of the village. For he went on:

" It's a warning off the rocks, eh ? So 'tis. Threlkelt and many anoder shepherd will tell you that, and mebbe if his tongue could run so lang he'd have something to say aboot a welcome too—the sort of weather he's glopping roond in. . . . And for aw t'oders, who is there to welcome ? "

I didn't tell him how many a time, dropping down

146

from the fells of an evening, it had been the most welcome sight I had looked on after hours of darkness and buffetings, and how it had more than once seemed to invite me over its threshold. But always as I drew nearer either its greeting did not seem intended for me, or else it was that my courage failed me.

In this state of indecision perhaps three or four years had passed away. The time had been too crowded to seek a friendship—to seek anything. All that was came unsought, some of the bounty by way of work, some in idleness. The mountains, even the neighbouring woods, even Dalethwaite, had for a while nothing to set against this plenty. But during the winter, and with increasing frequency as the following year went on, I had met the old woodman at all hours and under many conditions, until latterly our meetings had become an almost daily affair.

When, one day some months back, after a longer absence than usual, he had greeted me with the remark: " Hoots! You haven't been coming roond much of late—weather, likely? " and drove his spade in the ground, as though willing to make up all arrears, I felt that our intercourse was no longer a matter of mere form; and with this encouragement I never again spared any occasion of developing it. But thus far Dalethwaite had neither invited me to his cottage, nor so much as referred to it. My first visit was as unexpected to him as it was to me.

II

March had come in like a lamb, following a winter as gentle as itself. Days or weeks of frost and thaw had alternated; but in all goodly qualities the general opinion of the dale, ever reluctant to give praise on oath, averred that nothing had ever been experienced to match it. Dalethwaite concurred. The single dissentient voice, so he told me laughingly, was that of an old, bent, and palsied woman whose cottage he passed daily on the way to work, not rarely breaking his journey (but this I learned many years later when, Dalethwaite gone, the dale knew itself absolved from silence), to give a cheery " good-morning " or to do some small service of which age and solitude were in need. She, living in the long past, would have none of it. " How foalks talks! " she quavered. " It's a' bladder and clash. I' my young days they war a' like this, most ivry year—and sic a sight warmer too." But then, as Peter added, " She's a poor crinketty-cranketty old creature, is old Molly— always was given to blawin' cold when you blawed hot . . . and " (with lowered voice and pointing significantly to his head), " nut varra reet."

But Peter had his own contrary views regarding these first summerly days of March. I don't think appearances ever took him in, and least of all in the matter of weather. I had just joined him in a glade high up in the woods; his coat was off, pick and

148

spade lay unsoiled on the mossy turf at his feet;
and as I came suddenly upon him it looked verily
as though he, and the pipe he was filling, and the
glade and the sunshine, were agreed together on a
day's truancy. There was no sign of work done,
none of work contemplated. Even the tools couched
on moss cried out against him, mute parties to his
indolence. He had come to a tryst; he was already
too much in the spirit of it to put up a show of
refutation.

The glade was full of sunshine and sweet earthy
scents, and a little beck ran gurgling and splashing
from stone to stone with so small a voice that the
song hardly overflowed its banks. His back was
turned to me, and before speaking I knelt down,
dipped my hands in the ice-cold water, and pushing
them into the moss beneath, set free a million sparkling bubbles. Still on my knees I greeted him with
a sneering comment on his prophecy of yesterday.
He regarded me awhile in amused silence, slowly
withdrew a match from his waistcoat pocket, struck
it with considerable difficulty on the top of his boot,
lit his pipe at such length and with so much respiratory effort that it seemed doubtful if he would have
breath left to renew the conversation, and then, the
end of the match still flaming to a finish in the bowl,
he looked me full in the face and said:

"What are those aneroids of yours doing?

Mebbe the blenk of blue sky's put 'em a little wrang in their calculations."

Now the sting of this remark lay not so much in the word "aneroids," which in a gently mocking fashion he had adopted from me, nor in the use of the plural which, the truth though it was, was clearly used by Dalethwaite to express the scorn he felt for all such jee-jaws, but rather in its covert implication of the source of all the meteorological knowledge he ascribed to me. He had removed the pipe from his mouth between the two sentences, and now restored it, scrunching the mouthpiece desperately between his teeth, and flapping his cheeks in and out like a loose sail, though without restoring to it the smallest sign of life.

It seemed now my turn to jeer.

"The conflagration seems to have gone out, Dalethwaite. Perhaps you'd better wait until you have your fire to light it at."

He laughed.

"Aa'm a bit of a ninny-hammer at a pipe. Baccy's tricky stuff to deal wid. You nivver knaw the odds when you put a match to't, maist so wid the bit you've left ower from the last time. Flavour's all reet, reet to the verra end; and when the pipe's all cleared oot, and a fresh start's made, there's a sight of middling enjoyment to get through befwore you reach it."

By this time he had given up a further attempt, and after carefully pressing down with his finger the débris that remained from I know not how many previous smokes, he returned the pipe to an upper waistcoat pocket in silence.

But I saw there was something yet to come. I had learned to recognize a certain twinkle about the mouth as a sign that Dalethwaite had some definite purpose afoot and was of a mind to pursue it.

" Those aneroids," he began. " You've likely been consulting 'em, and tapping 'em, Aa guess, befwore you came oot? "

" Yes, and they're going up, all three of them," I replied triumphantly.

" Did they teall you where the wind was makking for? Or, mebbe, you didn't think on to ask them? "

I stood before this man then and on many an occasion since as one entirely at his mercy. Similar experiences befall most people, if they are fortunate in their acquaintance, at some period of life. To the schoolboy they come in the form of interviews in the head master's study, and there the fortune attaching to them follows its accustomed habit, and is only momentarily impressive. Both at the time and in long memory it is all a question of usage, of truth or tyranny, of whether the offender's garments are torn off or merely fall away. Before Dalethwaite they fell away. You might be stark naked, and know it,

but somehow he gave you the feeling that he didn't
—or knew, and finely disdained the advantage.

" Well, what about the wind? "

" North."

" Well, what else? "

" Snaw."

I looked through a network of branches upwards
to a wide expanse of cloudless sky. On one side a
gap opening southward towards the dale disclosed
near at hand a profile, green and splendid, with
many wrinkles, of the fell that guarded it, and beyond
and far away a gathering of high mountains, the laſt
of all, as always at this season, capped with snow.
Above them hung a single cloud, drawn lengthwise
as though a scroll holding some hidden legend. All
else above this screen of bare winter trees was radiant
sky, and its light brimmed over into the little dell
where the old woodman and I ſtood duelling.

" Snow! " I echoed. " Is it possible? "

" You've mebbe learnt by this day that maiſt
things are possible, not to say probable, wid the
weather in these parts. You may tak my word for't—
snaw afwore morning, and a gay sight of it too."

I sought further enlightenment, but Dalethwaite
bade me wait till the prophecy was fulfilled; and
gathering his things together, and putting his pipe
unlit into his mouth, he sauntered off into the depths
of the wood.

III

The woods were too tempting to leave for a while longer, and from Dalethwaite's companionship I turned contentedly enough to theirs. It was Stevenson to whom a night under the open sky told of the secret message that goes forth to bird and beast to prepare for the dawn while it is yet far off. It is a summons to which man has no key. A moment before the world slept; now it wakens. It begins, this drama of the day, with a little flutter of wings overhead, or stirring of the grass, or a few stray notes of song, quietly as though the passing of the great silence must be witnessed but not molested; for this is the hour of night's departure rather than of the day's advent. Or perhaps the earth is only about the business of morning toilet, and these movements of wing and foot, and the puny twitter here and there in hedge and coppice, are mere incidents in a prosaic rite. We must lean the ear to earth. Something of moment is happening; and while the curtain is still drawn, the preparations go forward for another day.

So in the woods this March morning. It was one of the days already come, perhaps a full month earlier than in most years, when we know that a season is passing, nay, that its successor is even now in possession; but usurped royalty is still at hand and must have the speeding due to him. There was not a sound far or near except that of my own footfall or the swish of dry brushwood as I pushed through, until I came to the lake side, where little ripples broke and murmured over the rocks. I looked from blue lake, its surface no longer as I had left it an hour ago, gleaming, motionless, but now rippled from end to end, to blue sky, and thought once again of Dale-thwaite's prophecy, and laughed. True the ripples came southward, but what of that? But indeed it was no time to weigh the future, good or evil. I turned back into the wood, away from home, for the spirit of idleness was still upon me. Last autumn's leaves scattered in places, in places piled into shape-less mounds by the wind, gave scarcely a sound under foot, so deep and lush was the mossy ground beneath them. The old pack-road, worn with many winters' storms, and once long ago trodden by man and beast journeying from the plumbago mines at dale-end to the market town, now lay deserted.

I thought if Gray, on that eventful walk in 1760, had only chosen this track he might have won this pleasure of the woods, only greater because autumn was there, and gained the village in the dale and the dish of ham and eggs without enduring the terrors he experienced, and at length succumbed to, on the other side the lake. What a price we pay for our conventionalities! Gray in the silk stockings and the plum-coloured breeches, and in the eighteenth

century, could no more face the deep woods than the
fear of impending rocks or of the fire at Peterhouse
that never occurred. For to traverse this path one
must go in stout country boots or take the risk of a
wetting.

But whatever its story of ancient traffic, to whatever indignities it might at seasons be put by the
becks that crossed it on their way to the lake, the
pack-road now lay deserted and sun-dried; deserted,
but not desolate; friendly rather as only a track long
beaten by many feet and now empty, dipping here
and there out of sight and reappearing to be lost at
last in the distance, can be.

All good and pleasant things lay about me—the
yielding turf under foot, radiant light filtering
through bare and crooked branches, silence, the
scent of prosperous earth, and their quiet memories
of unrecorded days. Some distance along the pack-
road I found that Dalethwaite must recently have
been working there—" tremenjously," as he called
it. But he was there no longer, nor was there sound
of him anywhere.

He had laid a great polished slab of stone (I
wondered whence it had come and how he had lifted
it) on one side of the track, so raised at either end
by baulks of timber carefully cut and shaped to
size, as to provide a footbridge over the beck—now
a mere trickle, but after rain broad and turbulent—

that ran across it. The word " rustic " fascinated him as the snake is said to fascinate birds; it lurked, snake-like, but a harmless snake, in all the constructive work of his hand, and when it popped out, as it would do on every hungry occasion, Dalethwaite stood before it as transfixed and helpless as the most fledgling prey. But he knew nothing of the suburban species, trained to juggling feats; his was the parent-stock, native, woodland, and altogether a good honest wholesome fellow. And this was one of his " rustic " bridges. The sawn ends of the timber were buttressed up with sods of grass, only the bark showing at either end, and where their rounded surfaces met the stone handfuls of moss had been pressed into the crevices. The casual wayfarer might have supposed the bridge as old as the road itself, and grown faithfully to all its uses.

I left the pack-road and following the runner straight up the hill came at length out on to the coach road. The sun had been clouded over some little while, though I had remarked the fact half unconsciously; but now, from this high point, I saw that heavy clouds had gathered northward and spread in a solid bank along the eastern hills of the dale. Again the thought of Dalethwaite and his prophecy came to my mind, and I heard the words over again, spoken with so much confidence: " Snaw! Snaw afwore morning, and a gay sight of it too."

IV

Whether awakened by it or not, or whether perhaps by the insistent ding of Dalethwaite's prophecy, I heard the wind many times during the night, and lay awake listening to the steady vibrant drone it made in the eaves, and to the lapping water. If the wind were high from whatever quarter, this last could always be detected among the many voices, but no great storm was necessary to make it the predominant voice when the wind drove from the north. At some small hour of the morning curiosity overcame other temptations, and I went to the window to look out—to look upon a world white with snow. It had come; and the first part of the prophecy, and I doubted not the second part also, was fulfilled even as it had been spoken.

As the morning wore on the wind increased mightily; the snow had ceased; sunshine in brief and splendid intervals came mysteriously between the immense glooms of earth and sky. After breakfast we had gone to the Point, and there hour after hour we kept watch, hurrying from one place to another to miss nothing of what was going on. A holiday was not declared because it was never asked for; it came, as our holidays were wont to come, by dispensation of Providence. We accepted. Sky and earth were performing for our pleasure. The spray was the *pièce de résistance*. It was harlequin, clown, pantaloon

—the mischievous fellow in a company of sober actors. It sprang into the air from nowhere, in a dozen places at once, as the clown is shot from the entrails of the stage; soared upwards or spread lengthwise, and came towards us in clouds of all shapes and sizes with incredible swiftness. Witches riding the storm was the description given by the children—hoards of them, but creatures of the day, and harmless. We watched them coming, our eyes chasing from one to another, our minds and tongues quick to search the issue. One thinned out and vanished before we had time to prophesy; another gathered in volume, came nearer, nearer, swung round, like a company at drill, and disappeared beyond the farther promontory; a third, more venturesome, more promising, reached our shore, passed us by on the other side, and was lost in the shade of trees. This was not playing the game. It was good, but only as a rehearsal, a prelude to the great event. And sure enough it came—one greater than we had bargained for. See! see! Excited hands were pointing to a cloud, a very monster, that had suddenly formed much nearer to us than any previous one. It was moving rapidly, not one, but many, this time like a flight of witches, grey and very old, each one leaping and dancing her own measure, but still holding hand to hand. It—they—were upon us before we knew. The last frantic leap,

and a yell; human voices mingling with theirs, and
—the deluge! I felt a little hand tighten on mine.
Glee was for a moment silenced into surprise, terror
—or perhaps it was only that the drench was so much
colder and wetter than Four-year-old had expected.

The rollicking spirit was abroad on land as on
the water. There, instead of water, it had unlimited
snow for plaything, deep powdery snow everywhere.
A cloud, like a puff of gunpowder, would suddenly
rise above the tree-tops, the wind tossing it hither
and thither before it melted into the grey light. A
dozen such, like the smoke of hidden fires, could
be seen at one moment over the whole extent of the
woods, except for these momentary frets so silent
and motionless under their pall of snow. One
wondered that no report, or other sign of any kind,
followed after; that this display of energy, so violent
it seemed, so disruptive, came in silence and went
out in silence; but the only sound was the steady
insistent drumming of the wind close at hand, and
the splash of water.

Again excited voices were raised, and we turned
our backs on lake and wood to look towards the dale.
Its steep western slopes lay to the tempest like a
meadow to the scythe; but when I had last looked there
was no mower at work, and the miles of snow pre-.
sented a smooth gleaming surface, giving to the immense shapes it covered an appearance of tranquillity

in deep and impressive contrast to the turmoil round them. Now all was changed. It seemed for a moment as though the fells were dissolving into mist before our eyes. Invisible hands had seized on their white covering and torn it to fragments, and the fragments were now racing in a dense inky cloud before the wind. Or was it this or the fells beneath it that moved? Except for the stubborn outlines, blurred but motionless, the illusion of mountains moving was irresistible—until gradually the mist cleared, and the fells once more and the snow over them resumed their imperturbable calm.

When interest in these great doings flagged we turned to snowballing or chased through the drifts, more fearsome in look than act, for beneath were deep springing tufts of heather to fall into. But as the day went on I grew restless, and a desire came upon me for adventure. One gets no nearer to a sunset or a night of stars than by watching, but to know a storm one must go into it. I determined to follow the track of this one.

Everything taken together, here are more good things than man could have had the conscience to ASK *of God.*

WILLIAM COBBETT

I

I SET out in the afternoon companionless, for under the conditions it seemed best to leave the dogs. It was a course so unexampled that the concerted efforts of the family were necessary to convince them. Across the meadow and just before diving into the wood I looked back. Conviction was not yet absolute, clearly, at least not with two of them. The wolf-hound and the Skye terrier were still craning their necks to get the last sight of my retreating figure, and still, I knew, expecting the whistle to set them free. The third, an Aberdeen, new to our life and most perseveringly addicted to living his own, had already turned tail and become engrossed in the novel possibilities of snow. I was leaving half the pleasure of a tramp behind, but wisely, as events showed.

Once clear of the wood and on the fell-side, I realized the impossibility of making plans. Generally the snow was not deeper than eight or ten inches; here and there were considerable patches of ground swept almost clear by the wind; in other places were correspondingly deep and difficult drifts either to plough through or to circumvent. These must

161

increase in number, and increase probably enormously in difficulty, higher up where the ground was more broken and more exposed to the wind.

For awhile I wandered on aimlessly—if wandering can be applied to such an arduous, clambering, and stumbling progress—only making steadily as far as practicable for higher and higher ground. But I soon discovered that a direction chosen indiscriminately was foolishness. I was expending valuable energy so rapidly that it was convincingly important to decide on a definite course and to adhere to it as closely as snowdrifts and inequalities of surface would allow. Even at the cost of immediate toil I determined to scramble straight up the fell to a bluff of rock that hung precipitately overhead, and thence to follow a track—in part a narrow sheep-track, in part the bed of a mountain torrent—which would take me, if I could strike it, over the shoulder of the fell. That point gained I should be content to make a headlong descent.

The climb was more toilsome and beset with more difficulties than I had anticipated; the foothold was in most places so precarious, the drifts so deep and unsuspected, and the snow so yielding, that anything approaching a straight course was impossible. To gain my rock I had to tack as methodically as a sailing-boat making against the wind.

This was the most exposed situation in the climb.

I was up among the winds—not one wind, but many—one, a robustious periwig-pated fellow from the north, who, having swept these miles of snow to a surface ribbed and smooth as the seashore, was now hissing and snarling across it as though, his work finished, he were made desperate by his own unused strength; and against him others would start up in momentary challenge from every quarter out of gaps and crevices as I drew nearer to them:

> Winds thwarting winds, bewildered and forlorn.

Where they and the slayer met together there was confusion, the snow smothering them like the dust of battle, wonderful to behold from a distance, but in the thick of it, scourging like a cat-o'-nine-tails, and biting down to one's very bones. It was such an experience that very soon the chief concern of my adventure was to escape it.

Yet the labour, severe and unremitting though it was, only sufficed to keep me from becoming uncomfortably cold—as the phrase goes, to keep life in me. Or rather, I seemed to be stretched out—a rack stretching me—between equator and pole; a consuming heat possessing my body at one moment, at the next surrendering it miserably to a shiver; my feet ice-cold; my hands and ears tingling between the two extremes. Half my pains was now the difficulty of apportioning the uses of my hands between clinging on to any hold within reach and beating them together to restore warmth. But a minute's pause from sheer breathlessness, sheer fatigue, or in the recovery from a more than usually ungainly fall, convinced me that the least of evils was to keep steadily going.

The bluff was at length gained, and on reconnoitering it I discovered a deep narrow gully on its lee side, a mere chink between immense glistening slabs of rock, that came close together overhead, to form, with the snow that had lodged between, an almost complete roof. I swung myself down to the opening and crept in. In summer it would have felt like walking into one's grave; it was now like walking out of it. Relief was instantaneous, the warmth, the peace and quiet, the unutterable silence that first told me the trials I had gone through of mere noise. I could chafe my hands, my ears, at leisure. . . .

I knew now the extent of my weariness. But the prospect of home, and a hot bath, and tea, and a log fire, and the story to tell over it, was near enough to hasten my departure. I had decided on the course to follow. The track I had expected to find started on the other side of the gully, a few yards away, and ran, as I had noticed before entering the shelter, like a terrace-walk towards the shoulder of the fell, about two hundred feet higher up. The arduous part of the journey was over; once round the shoulder

I should be descending almost down to the dale on a southern slope, protected from the wind, and probably clear of drifts.

It was even as I had surmised, except that I had miscalculated the time of the descent by not allowing for steep and slippery surfaces, for recovery from headlong and painful tumbles, and for the constant wearying business of extricating my legs and feet from the hidden bracken and, even worse, the boulders. But I was bent on making the utmost haste possible. Night was fast coming on, and the spasmodic exhilarations that temper the first stages of weariness were petering out and leaving me in possession of a dogged menacing fatigue.

It was less than half-way in the descent that my calculations went astray. I had just scrambled round a projecting rock when something—some sound, or movement, or perhaps only that familiar instinct that invites one to look round a corner—caused me to turn my head. Not fifteen paces away a sheep was standing, deep in snow to the belly, and snow massed on its back, its appearance made more comical by an expression of half sheepish foolishness, half blank amazement. She started to an immediate attitude of *qui vive*, disguised momentarily by a twitch of the neck, as though precipitate flight had occurred to her as the only sheep-like procedure. But she was fixed immovably. I forgot my own predicament, my own weariness, everything before the spectacle of that sheep—that 'scape-goat—alone, outcast, burdened under its weight of snow.

After staring at each other in mutual wonder for I know not how long, she suddenly turned her head towards the farther end of the rock I had just clambered down. My eyes followed in the same direction. There under shelter of the rock, and close beside it, on a patch of green turf surrounded by a low wall of snow, lay a puny lamb. I could see it was but a few hours born. The head was lifted a little above the ground, but the neck seemed too weak to support it. Its eyes were turned towards me, but they were expressive neither of apprehension, surprise, nor enquiry.

II

There was only one thing to be done, but how to do it? The mother-sheep could safely be left; the lamb must be got away. The sheep atmosphere had infected me: I began with immense diligence and immense futility to think of the different farmers in the dale, which grazed on these home-fells, and which didn't; to which the lamb was most likely to belong. . . . How long I was bemused in the futile enquiry I don't know; but at length a gleam of reason revealed the hard truth that it was not within my capacity to reach any of the farms. I must carry it home. Then there flashed into my mind like an inspiration the thought of Dalethwaite. His cottage lay almost in the direct line of my return.

I picked up the little unresisting bundle, tucked it inside my coat-breast, and set off. The sheep bleated, made fruitless plunges into deeper snow, and I suppose stuck there, more snow-logged, more utterly baffled than before. I remember her bleating followed me a very short while. I wondered at this; I wondered why I was left so suddenly with the lonely sound of the wind across the snow. I held my burden carefully with one arm to support it.

I knew I was holding it gently, though both the thought and the act seemed to arise out of themselves, and not to concern me. But under the stimulus of a new excitement my progress went on for a time more cheerfully. I became interested in picking out my way so as to avoid unnecessary jolts and tumbles. Strange errant fancies came into my mind. They, too, seemed to arise independently of me, like dim figures passing at a distance, which I might notice casually or not, but recognition being expected neither on my side nor theirs. The nearest thought to me was of deepening weariness, a desire to rest awhile. . . . The growing darkness encouraged a wish to sleep. . . .

A steady square of light appeared below me. I knew it must be Dalethwaite's kitchen window.

I remember smiling, though I was not conscious either of surprise or pleasure. The question shaped itself: Should I ever reach it?—and then with a complete indifference I found the question was turning over and over in my mind. My arm was aching. I had to use the other hand to support the lamb while I eased the position. The puny creature was safe at any rate. . . .

Other thoughts came, and memories, flitting before my mind like wraiths, grey and bodiless; and sometimes they recurred, and recurred again, with greater vividness, like summer lightning, playing for a moment as it were over the surface of this stark grim business of making headway, and then vanished and left me once more alone with it. I remembered the dogs, as I had last seen them, heads and ears lifted expectantly. Negligible incidents of the day, of long previous days, came into my mind. . . . I should see Dalethwaite's cottage at last. I wondered what he would say, how he would receive me.

Thinking of him, the prophecy of yesterday, spoken in the glade with the sunshine streaming into it, disturbed me into a momentary interest: "Snaw, and a gay lot of it too." I stopped to peep under my coat for the first time, at a sudden impulse. I recollected with a sort of impersonal apprehension that I had not noticed any movement. My hand encountered warmth. The lamb was nestling close to my side. I could not see its face, but I felt it snuggling more firmly against my arm.

This conscious effort, though so trivial, and the proof that all was well with my burden, quickened me once more into keenness, into life. The effect soon passed—I know not how soon—and I was back once more with my thoughts, with the questions that came dully and were never answered, the old ones returning over and over again, and now and then a new one slipped in among them, giving me a vacant surprise, anxiety, amusement. They were all now, as it were, encompassed by the desire to lie down— anywhere—now. For some reason the thought of doing it deliberately agitated me, and I decided it would be so much easier when next I stumbled not to save myself.

Even while other thoughts were flitting backwards and forwards in my mind, I found myself busily arguing the reasonableness of resting—it should be for no more than a few minutes, I kept on assuring myself—five minutes—I was fascinated by the number five. I was now repeating "five" as though it were the toll of a muffled bell, though it no longer had any reference to the notion that gave rise to it or any special concern for me. Something—it never shaped itself in words—impelled me onwards. Everything was vanishing but the simple idea of my utter weariness, of sensations I had never before experienced—possessing me, beating me down. And then they came upon me with such force, such a vivid surprised conviction, as to stir me to one last determined effort. . . . I realized now that the wind had dropped. I was indifferent. The only sound was of my own movements, and it seemed to be telling over and over again all I was, all my miseries present and to come. . . .

Nearing the valley the drifts became deeper and more frequent. The heather and bracken too grew more luxuriantly. I remembered that the next stretch was difficult even in summer, in daylight. . . . Suddenly I thought of the cottage and raised my eyes from peering down at the snow—endless hours of peering into it—I seemed to have known nothing else. The nearness of the light startled me. One window was ablaze. I stopped for a moment to think what it all meant; and while I stood looking a door opened, and a flood of light went out over the snow. The figure standing in the doorway was Dalethwaite's. Then the door closed again, and in the stillness I could hear a bolt drawn.

III

" Well, Aa nivver! Whativver is't? Mans! come in, come in! Nay, doan't think of saying anything —just sit here alongside the fire. Aa'll have a cup of tea ready for you in a twinkle. A lamb? Aa nivver! . . . Whativver does it all mean? Here

lie you doon on the sofa. Don't bother aboot the
lamb, whativver; Aa'll have a basket and a sup of
milk for it in naw time. Aa happen to have a good
fire, and the watter's boiling eall ready. You can hear
it birling a welcome to you. But Aa'm. . . . Well,
Aa nivver!"

*   *   *

I awoke. Perhaps I had slept out my sleep, or
perhaps it was the subdued level tone of a voice not
pitched for hearers that had wakened me. I must
have wakened without making the least movement,
because the voice went on undisturbed. This was
not surprising, any more than my immediate acceptance of the situation, for I had been groping about
half-consciously on the borderland of sleep and
dreams for a long time, or so it seemed—it seemed
indeed I had been doing nothing else—never
straying deeper in, or till this moment of escape,
getting farther out. And in that twilight state the
two directions seemed equally open to me, and
neither, whichever I took, was likely to disturb my
preparedness and unconcern. Though the knowledge brought no pain, no apprehension, I knew that
I was infinitely weary, sore, indifferent.

I was lying full-length on an upholstered and
cushioned oak settle drawn slant-wise across the
hearth, my head raised on pillows, a rug or quilt
thrown over me from feet to shoulders. A log fire
blazed and crackled in the open grate. It had been

recently replenished. Yes, I was sure I had noticed
the fire being gently ſtirred to make way for the new
logs, and the sudden swish and crackle that kept the
thought it had aroused dinging for a while longer in
my head with a diſtant, dreamy recognition: A fire!
a log-fire—It is there, for me—After all that snow,
miles of it! Ugh! The shooting flames threw the
end of the low room into alternate light and shadow.
It was entrancing to watch the sudden appearances
in the gloom, their outlines lengthening and wavering
into fantaſtic shapes, ſtretching out, narrowing,
fading. . . .

I craned my head a little forward. On the farther
side of the hearth lay a wicker basket, with a lamb
curled up inside; and near it was a basin, with a
tube, or some such thing, hanging over the brim.
A table ſtood a little diſtance away on which was a
lamp heavily shaded, and beside it sat Peter Dalethwaite, his right elbow reſting near the edge, his
hand raised to support the bent head and pushed
deep into the lank grey hair, which all the while he
teased out reſtlessly through his fingers. The other
arm was hidden, but it lay extended over the table,
for I could hear the hand drumming incessantly on
its surface, firmly and rhythmically, as though
keeping time with great matters. An open book lay
in front of him. I could see its white pages and gilt
edges, for Dalethwaite sat a little tilted to one side,

his face silhouetted in the bright space between a dark shoulder and the gloom beyond. He was wearing—the first time I had seen them in use— iron-rimmed spectacles, so low down on the nose that he seemed as likely to be looking over as through them. His face and the open page were the only illumined objects between the darkness of the far end of the room and the flickering firelight intercepted by the stonework of the chimney.

All this I took in at a glance, and at the same moment I was thinking with a quiet satisfied pleasure: Here at last Dalethwaite is at home to me.

And the reading continued without pause, every word, every syllable pronounced slowly and distinctly, in the subdued and even tone of one who reads aloud from a habit of childhood rather than of deliberate purpose. It was more chant than reading. So far I had not given a thought to the words. My eyes were fascinated by the picture before me, my ears by the solemnity and impressiveness of mere meaningless words rolled out with that splendid northern burr. The voice pitched so low, so unvarying in emphasis, seemed to me in its very monotonousness a chant more moving than any I had before heard—neither of minster nor oratory, nor of anything associated with the rutted habits and traditions of men and churches, but of the mountains. Dalethwaite was worshipping, he believed alone, and I was overhearing his worship. Much as I was drawn into his mood, it seemed wrong to share it unasked and unknown to him. Should I call out? But I had already forgotten the question and was intent listening.

" *Forasmuch therefore as your treading is upon the poor, and ye take from him burdens of wheat, ye have built houses of hewn stone, but ye shall not dwell in them: ye have planted pleasant vineyards, but ye shall not drink wine of them. For I know your manifold transgressions, and your mighty sins: they afflict the just, they take a bribe, and they turn aside the poor in the gate from their right. Therefore the prudent shall keep silence in that time, for it is an evil time.*"

The voice had grown a trifle louder as it proceeded, like one of our becks gathering strength as it nears the lake, and then lapsed into silence. The pause seemed an immense, a magical stillness. It could only have been momentary, and yet in my consuming interest I wondered if it were ever going to end and if I were to be cheated of more. A word half-formed, perhaps a whole word, showed that the reading was being resumed when, to my astonishment, Dalethwaite raised his head from the supporting hand and softly turned round to look at me. I noticed that his face was bent downwards in order to peer over the rims of his spectacles. But I was too quick for him; his deliberate movements had given me time to close my eyes and feign an undisturbed sleep; though had he been nearer I felt he must have seen the active flickering of my eyelids. Nay, they twitched so violently that I had to argue myself into the assurance that they could not be seen at this distance and in the dancing light, even by his keen eyes.

For awhile there was perfect silence, broken only by the measured wheezy tick of a grandfather clock somewhere in the darkness. My suspense, burdened with the effort to keep still, grew painful. At last I heard a chair softly scraping on the stone floor, and then I felt rather than heard Dalethwaite creeping stealthily towards me. I knew he was bending over me. I knew he had either pulled his spectacles off or dragged them lower down on his nose. I knew he was searching me like some watcher of the skies. More distressing still, I knew my eyelids were flickering more and more violently—so violently that I had to pull my face awry to control them; and to this was added a threatening of other facial contortions, between a desire to laugh outright and a desire to perpetuate the fraud. For curiously enough at that moment the humorousness of the situation was uppermost in my mind, and tricked me as a similar imp would trick Charles Lamb at funerals. I should have been so completely master of it too if I had realized how much my face was in shadow.

I began to doubt if I could hold out a moment longer, when relief came. Dalethwaite was evidently satisfied with his vigil. I knew he had moved away before I heard a log being laid quietly on the fire; and a moment later I again heard the chair rubbing and jarring on the floor.

At this point I felt it safe to open my eyes. He had settled down in his chair, his hand was smoothing the page, more from habit than necessity, his forefinger moving slowly down it to find the place. The reading began, in a voice so much lower than before that I could catch the words only very imperfectly. But suddenly, at a turn of the page, they became louder, and more resonant than loud, with some touch of fierceness in them. His hand had gone back to its former position, the fingers spread farther into the ruffled hair, grasping a mass where it was thickest, and spasmodically tugging and re-grasping it by turns, as he read:

"*I hate, I despise your feast days, and I will not smell in your solemn assemblies. Though ye offer me burnt offerings, and your meat offerings, I will not accept them; neither will I regard the peace offerings of your fat beasts. Take thou away from me the noise of thy songs: for I will not hear the melody of thy viols. But let judgment run down as waters, and righteousness as a mighty stream.*"

He read on to the end of the chapter, dwelling

on its laſt words as one clinging to something of great price, and when it was done pushed the book a little away from him. But now both hands were raised to support the head that bent towards them, and both lay motionless, almoſt buried, in the tousled locks. Again the only sounds in the room were the ticking of the grandfather clock and, close beside me, the low fluſtering crackle of a log not wholly seasoned that Dalethwaite had but recently thrown on the fire. In contraſt to this quiet was the dancing firelight playing fitfully among the deep shadows. Some minutes went by, and ſtill the grey head was buried in the outſtretched fingers of both hands. I knew that Dalethwaite was deep in some affairs of his own.

IV

How long this ſtate of things would have continued I don't know, had not an unexpeſted occurrence ended it. From the neighbourhood of the clock there arose, without the smalleſt forewarning, a loud ſtrident wheeze, running up to a crescendo of the moſt dismal, whirring, discordant sounds I had ever heard—or heard only once, when, in passing at nightfall through an Arab village there came from one of its squalid alleys a noise of the same terrifying charaſter, whether human in origin or not I was utterly at a loss to determine, nor did I wait to inveſtigate. Perhaps because of my weakened

M

condition the effect now was not less desolating, until a moment later the sound culminated in one more homely and familiar. The clock was striking the hour. One! The strike was painfully deliberate. I was straining on the sound. A flood of anxiety came over me. Its drawled " one " was maddening —was there no more to follow? Two!—Three!— and there it stopped.

" Dalethwaite! " I shouted, raising myself with difficulty—" Whatever time is it? "

The old man sprang up from his chair and came towards me.

"Ey, you've had a fine sleep. How are you feeling?"

" But, Dalethwaite, the time! Think of them at home."

" That's all reet," he said soothingly—" that's all reet. You may be easy in your mind aboot that. Naw need to trouble aboot that, whativver. . . . You've slept like a bairn—nivver so much as turned ower, except yance, and then you turned in your sleep." He saw my eyes stray towards the lamb. " Yes," he continued, " Aa was terribly afeared the yammering he set up when he began to thaw, poor cold doddering slip of life! would wakken you. But it didn't—not a blenk. Aa soon quieted it wid a drop of warm milk. Bless you, it took to the bottle as gradeley as you took to the sofa, and no pressing nayder."

He laughed, and came nearer, his face all gentleness and solicitude. He was looking at me with the closeſt scrutiny, and I thought not altogether with satisfaction; but he was underſtanding enough not to ply me with queſtions. " Aa'm juſt going to mak you a cup of tea," he said.

I did not queſtion myself; there was no more occasion in my own case than in his. The liſtless dreamy intereſt I was taking in watching Dalethwaite's movements, in watching the flames flicking among the logs, my eye held by one trivial object till another more trivial drew it in any new direction that could be acquired without effort—my utterly passive and submissive attitude towards everything I looked on, and equally so towards my own vagrant thoughts, and yet my mild absorbing intereſt in everything— all this had meaning enough if I was in the mood for enquiry. It was not less convincing when, Dalethwaite having advanced the preparations for our early meal, I experienced the immense relief of not having to follow him any longer in his wanderings about the room, but could let my eyes browse quietly, without diſtractions and without the leaſt physical effort, on the picture of the old man ſtooping over the lamb, feeding it.

" Aa had no bottle," he explained; " but it was verra fortunate Aa happen't to have this bit of tube. It has been used for the seamm thing afwore, two years gan, and it serves weel enoo. Leaſtways the lamb knaws naw difference. For you knaw," he added slyly—in reference I suppose to certain contemptuous opinions I had often expressed, to his great amusement—" You knaw lambs are only sheep in the meakk."

Over our tea I gained a more explicit assurance of the position at home; but of the manner of conveying the news I learned nothing. Dalethwaite could feint and parry, could avoid diplomatic traps, as unobtrusively as a De Comines. He used his skill here, but at laſt, driven into a corner, he condescended to the clumsy device of coughing, of ſtirring the fire at great length, even of going hurriedly into the adjoining room to recover something that was not wanted. When these laſt refuges seemed likely to fail, he turned on me with the unexpected and almoſt ſtern requeſt:

" And now Aa want to knaw whativver you were doing ower Holm Crag on sic a night."

I quailed before him. The thought occurred to me of a bewigged Judge, and the Book, and a terrifying demand for whole truths; and, as muſt often happen in such situations, I could only think of trifling irrelevancies.

" I went for a walk—for the fun of the thing."

" A walk! The fun of the thing! Aa fancy the fun was well ower afwore you reached this door."

"It was, Peter. But listen. I did go for fun—though fun isn't the right word. It was not fool-hardiness—I never suspected danger, never gave it a thought. The storm in the morning had simply got into my head, like wine. I felt nothing could content me short of the full draught. Did you ever hear the story of the farmer new to rent-dinners who swallowed off his thimbleful of liqueur, and, beckoning to the flunkey, said: 'Here, young fellow, I'll tak some of that in a mug'? Well, I can't tell you better than that. Strong beverage as it was, I had a fierce desire to drink to the dregs. . . ."

"It was the quantity," I went on, "that proved too much for me—and remember the quantity was so much more than I or anyone could have foreseen. A lamb, nothing less than the little chap in the basket, was thrown into it too—remember that. The drink was forced down me in the end—past exhilaration, on to the stage of sheer drunkenness, of fuddled head, of miserably shambling legs. It's a story, as you see, Peter, of innocent——"

"Backsliding, Aa think it might be called best," he interpolated with gusto.

"Yes, backsliding indeed, especially down that first slope—not intentional debauch."

"But whativver meadd you go aw that way?"

"It was all the getting back," I explained. "The pull up to the Crag was heavy work, but I felt fresh and keen as mustard after a few minutes' rest. I believed the work was over, and the fun just beginning. That's where I miscalculated. I hadn't bargained for all those tumbles or for the ghastly business of disentangling feet and legs from the undergrowth, to say nothing of stumbling into drifts, sometimes up to my hips—and least of all for the lamb."

Whether he wanted more or not, I was exhausted. Excitement had borne me thus far and went out like a guttering candle. The old man, till now composedly listening to the recital, turned a quick glance on me.

" Lie doon," he said, " have your headd reet law doon. You'll feel better after anoder sleep."

Long have I loved what I behold,
The night that calms, the day that cheers;
The common growth of mother-earth
Suffices me—her tears, her mirth,
Her humblest mirth and tears.

WORDSWORTH

I

IT then seemed to me strange I had never visited
Dalethwaite before. A growing intimacy, and on
my side a growing affection, the man's own character, in which a feast of good things was plentifully
spread and an ample reserve promised, the vague
allurements of surprise and discovery, and all these
" at home " in a long, low cottage, white-walled and
green-slated, beyond a wide billowy pasture that
sloped irregularly to its own door, spread out into a
shelf for its reception, and then after providing a long
slip of palisaded garden, mounted rapidly towards a
splendid head of fell, down which a watercourse raced
and tumbled till it reached the precincts of the cottage
and was lost in the level bents—how I had come so
long to neglect these inducements I cannot say.

l have known forbidding cottages in many English
counties, just as one may travel with a solitary
passenger in a railway carriage and feel silence the
lesser of two stupidities; others that say nothing and
invite nothing; and again others that exhale, if the

183

hour be discreetly chosen, a compelling welcome. And of these last I had already made the acquaintance of many in the dale. If the passer-by realized the lonely drab life within he would knock more often perhaps, and know how much he had to give—and receive—and how pleasantly. But often as I had looked with interest towards Dalethwaite's house as I passed along the lane, or on more than one occasion dropped down the fell almost to his back door, to remark with envy how the mountain torrent had come at that distance to shape at last a channel of turbulent water along one end of his garden, something—some unchallenged inhibition—had kept me from entering. The familiar Dalethwaite of the woods was not one and the same with the proprietor of this wayside cottage, yet sufficiently the same to make the attempt more difficult than in the case of a casual acquaintance.

The feeling persisted even after my eventful and forced intrusion. Dare I trespass further on the strength of such an unceremonious occurrence? Would the welcome in the woods, the cordiality of which there was no possible doubt, be extended to the cottage? The question grew more insistent because the desire grew; and time enough was given me to ponder it—the slow, self-centred voyaging time of convalescence after illness. Though I had been of a mind to let it rest, Dalethwaite contrived otherwise. He called daily. On some days he forgot his reserve, his air of timid indifference, and came morning and evening. The lady of the house schemed whenever possible to answer his almost inaudible knock. Her relief from nursing lay in the few moments' entertainment of the old woodman's visit, and the manner of it. Hat in hand and face a little bent towards the ground, he would lift a crooked finger to the forelock of rugged hair, then raise his head to a soldierly attention, as though by the contrast to show a sudden access of resolution, and—say nothing, still trusting to the frank blue eyes to reveal his purpose under cover of bushy eyebrows. There was a pause, occupied by a play of shyness, hesitancy, self-distrust, ill-concealing the urgency of mood beneath. At length the feet shuffled a little. It was hard to resist this physical corroboration of the crisis that was going on, this reinforcement of mute questioning and appeal. But these were recognized signs, and a malicious enjoyment found them too entertaining to give immediate assistance.

" Aa've been wondering. . . ."

" It is good of you, Dalethwaite. He's going on well, after a capital night—the best so far."

" Aa'm glad." A pause—something still to say. " Has he heard them? They've come—the sand-pipers. You'll mebbe teall him. The tenth of April —Aa've nivver knawn them earlier—yan pair aff

Brandley, anoder nigh Great Bay. Likely he'll hear the whistle to-morrow morning ahint the Point."

" Thanks; it will be welcome news. I'll tell him."

At this, the curious quiet glance of interrogation I knew so well would come into the old woodman's face, and, satisfied, dissolve into a genial, contented smile—a sequence that invariably led to renewed effort. Edging a little away he continued:

" It'll be ahint the Point first; naw pleass so likely. It would be there this morning Aa don't doobt—it's ivver the first pleass. . . . A good neet—Aa'm verra glad—there's nothing like it. Mebbe to-morrow he'll be listening aboot day breakk." Then recalling the price this early watch exacted in the case of an invalid, he added with becoming gravity: " But best be sleeping; Aa'd nivver let on; in anoder day or two he'll be hearing it for himself all day lang. But Aa'll leave it with you."

This concluded the morning's business; and, his finger once more lifted to his forelock, Dalethwaite reinstated the shapeless wide-brimmed hat and set off towards the woods.

II

If ever a man feel reconciled to an illness and exceeding friendly towards life it is during convalescence, the convalescence that " suffers not the tediousness of a creeping restitution, nor the inconvenience of Surgeons and Physicians, watchfulness and care, keepings in and suffering trouble, fears of relapse and the little relics of a storm," as Jeremy Taylor has it. The tussle is over and he is victorious. Every genial failing of humanity is pandered to from morning to night. He has but to receive, and receptiveness is precisely the mood in which the previous trial has left him.

> See the wretch, that long has tost
>   On the thorny bed of pain,
> At length repair his vigour lost,
>   And breathe and walk again:
> The meanest flowret of the vale,
> The simplest note that swells the gale,
> The common sun, the air, the skies,
> To him are opening Paradise.

The senses are washed clean as the air in morning dew, and all we look on, hear, taste, has the excitement of a new discovery, except that enjoyment is heightened from its call back to earliest memories and associations, some of them vague and merged in subconsciousness, others vivid and particular. The body is too weak to obtrude its rough habits and ruder inclinations on a spirit quietened and chastened by suffering; and hope is now less a new growth, springing from soil however favourable, than a radiance spread over the whole of life. It is good to waken and remember; good to waken and know that the business of the day is to go one step nearer to recovery, and is easy enough to suggest neither effort nor apprehension.

Like other pleasures, this of convalescence comes more keenly in youth, but it is my experience of the old and the young alike, of luxurious homes, and homes hidden from the sunshine, grey, scanty, and troubled—" God knows how utter grey! "—that no other pleasure comes to the heart more universally or more compellingly, and is so little dependent on outward circumstance. It comes too so entirely unsought.

From one window, long, low, and unshadowed, I could look down the whole length of the lake towards the immense bulk of Skiddaw; another opened directly on to an old battered oak, whose gnarled branches cut into shifting tormented shapes a deep fringe of trees, and fells receding and climbing behind them to the sky; while a third gave more intimately, it gave back beneficently all I had recently lost—our own curve of bay and foreshore, our own rocks and gorse and heather, and the Scotch firs in two sombre masses, with an arm of the lake running between them. Here was plenty enough for convalescence.

Presently, while spring still delayed its coming, a missel-thrush built her nest in the oak tree close at hand. By that time I was sitting up in my armchair, so arranged that with my feet on the hearthstone I was no more than six or seven feet away, and could watch, partially screened by a curtain, every stage and every detail of the achievement. This stroke of good fortune robbed me of some of the vague and wandering happiness of convalescence by concentrating for the time being all my thoughts on to itself. What a combination of skill, eagerness, patience, persistence, watchfulness it was! In the five or six days from start to finish there was, while daylight lasted, not a moment's pause in the tireless energy, neither for food nor rest, unless indeed the labourer found the opportunity for one or the other during her absence, sometimes unduly prolonged, in search of building material. But now at the seat of operations the display of energy was amazing, and to it was lent a certain ferociousness by the thrusts and tugs that seemed to put the frail structure in immediate jeopardy, and by the glaring eyes, now concentrated on the work, now feverishly darting from side to side to spy or to quieten some suspected danger. But of all these movements the sudden flight was the most impressive; one moment sedulously labouring as though this stage of the work were an endless business, to which she had settled down with unquestioning resignation, the next vanishing, without effort, without the smallest preparation, so it seemed, body and spread wings clear of the one bough, clear of all the numberless boughs and twigs between her and the open sky. I followed the swift flight, swift and resolute, among the neighbouring trees, over the bay, till it was lost on the farther shore.

This was a passing show; the doings of lake, fell, and sky were inexhaustible and constant. I had but to push my chair from one corner of the hearth to the other to command them all. And March and April are ever the months when most is happening. They are the youth of the year. Time later for tranquillity, for contemplation, for a beauty however perfect that embodies an impalpable joy of dreams, into which it merges and is itself lost. Now is the hour of " glad animal movements," soon enough to be put by. There are intervals of rest, but the pause is full of effervescent mirth and of preparation for the next escapade. The blue sky is given up to a mad race of cloud. An east wind comes over the crags that shelter the dark still water immediately beneath them: I see it drop far off with a splash and ride triumphantly on crested wings across the lake, and the beating of the wings, as they fall spent on the rocks, is carried up to my window. At times, even with that high cliff to baulk its violence, it tears the waves to tatters, and a scene that was a moment earlier vividly clear is smudged with clouds of spray, more destructive to the view because of the sunlight woven into them.

To this scene the splendid pile of Skiddaw is the background. Impassive at all hours and in its own shapeliness, it repays the long watches from my window most generously by recording from hour to hour faithfully the constant changes of light and shadow, of storm and cloud. He shows nothing of the frivolities of lesser hills; every change is but another phase of dignity and solemnity. That huge chasm, as it seems at this distance, spreading like a lotus from base to summit, is the home of eternal gloom, deepened suddenly as the clouds gather about his top, and withdrawing again as the light strengthens, like a mist dissolving, though never withdrawing far enough to remove, but only to soften, the contrasting beauty of lights and shadows.

He came nearer and more companionably too when I remembered that no other English mountain is associated with so many great English names. I could follow, these six miles away, the line men take in climbing past the little white hut, on to his interminable shoulder, to the last high summit. It is no Everest—no more indeed than a good day's tramp; and yet there was wonder and adventure even Everest does not possess in thinking of the men who had long ago taken the path and reached the summit—yes, and the men who hadn't, but who had still laid an offering at the foot. For Southey, pedestrian in many things, who lived so long at the gates of this mountain, it remained a grand tour; he acted guide to men greater and less than him, though all of names good to remember; he played host to hungry and thirsty guests when the toil of the climb was over;

and conducted pagan rites in right good fashion to celebrate on its topmost crest the victory of Wellington and of Waterloo. Coleridge and Wordsworth had both tramped over Skiddaw and commemorated him either in good letters or in good poetry, I know not how often. Lamb came once, and conquered and was conquered, bringing Mary along with him to share the victory, if not the defeat. For Charles at any rate was an unmitigated and intransigeant townsman, and had to be won. " The lighted shops of the Strand and Fleet Street, the innumerable trades, tradesmen, and customers, coaches, waggons, playhouses; all the bustle and wickedness round about Covent Garden . . . have I not enough without your mountains?" And (still to the poor, misguided, assailed but unrepentant Wordsworth, sitting to some purpose among them)—" I do not envy you, I should pity you, did I not know that the mind will make friends with anything." But in the end he was induced to leave his " old book-stalls, Jeremy Taylors, Burtons on Melancholy, and Religio Medicis on every stall," to pay a visit to Coleridge, and—to climb Skiddaw. Mary, with her London ways, London pavement feet, was wearied by the time she had got half-way up—" But " (Lamb himself recounts the incident) " we came to a cold rill—than which nothing can be imagined more cold, running over cold stones—and with the reinforcement of a draught of cold water she surmounted it most manfully." His and her conquest. The other the mountain won: " Glorious creatures, fine old fellows, Skiddaw, etc., I never shall forget ye. . . . It was a day that will stand out like a mountain, I am sure, in my life."

Skiddaw is a host in himself, but I like him the better for these tales he can tell one after another, and best of all for the tale of another of his acquaintances, the youngest in years of them all, and soon to die. It was John Keats. Whether such a trial of endurance was worth while for him, who shall say? The forethought of the guide, who had brought a flask of rum with him, probably saved the exploit from failure. It was drawn upon to the extent of two glasses going, and one returning, " mixed, mind ye, with mountain water." So rejuvenated Keats too reached the summit. " I felt," he wrote, " as if I were going to a Tournament."

If confinement to one's bedroom restricts the field of vision, the loss has its recompense. How infinitely pleasant and friendly become the things nigh at hand! The carpet of heather was to my eyes a new birth, and the wind went over it, and the low sun gave it deep and strange colours. I marked the first celandine, and then another, until, a few sunny days hence, patches of the green turf were starred with them. Tits blue and ox-eye were busy with the last of the cocoanuts, broken into many shapes and curiously suspended in order to display their skill in acrobatics. One nut poised less perilously was on more than one occasion a scene of confusion. A sparrow settled on it, and then, so far gratified at initial success, perked his head in various directions to make sure the way was clear, and proceeded to the final evolution of clinging to the rim head downwards. He failed—he failed ignominiously—but tried again. All he achieved was to set the nut swinging and plunging as though a mighty wind had arisen. Later a robin made the attempt; with him was more deftness, but no greater success. But what he lost in frustrated hopes he took out in envy and all uncharitableness, returning times without number to drive away the tits that were prosperously gathering the food he himself could not reach.

Yes, as I discovered, there were more sights for a day's delectation than can be told. This restricted world beneath my windows was full of them, some turbulent and a little adventitious as though born of another order, like this of squabbling birds; others shy and discreet, native to the ground, that waited on a beneficent moment for deliverance. These were accompanied by sounds as welcome as themselves—I think more welcome. They came with less effort; they came by night as by day— this wind soughing in the heavy plumes of the firs, these waves lapping in the rocks. And one day, as Dalethwaite prophesied, I heard the sandpiper calling.

III

Those who have not themselves gone from stage to stage of convalescence would never believe the happy adventure it is; and none other, I fancy, gives more complete self satisfaction. Never could vanity be on better terms with itself. " What a piece of work is a man! how infinite in faculty! . . . in apprehension how like a god! "—he believes it all as he progresses on the prosperous way from sickness to health. " In form and moving how express and admirable! in action how like an angel! "—of this, perhaps, for the time being, he is less sure. He can dismiss it as irrelevant, and without loss to his enchantment. The later stages introduce new elements. His world widens with immense and startling rapidity. In wandering from room to room, associations coming thick and fast, link him up with all past associations and memories, and he sees his life spread beneath him as from a serene height.

The second day of my arrival downstairs was celebrated by a chat with Dalethwaite. He had had no warning, but even while the usual enquiry conducted in much the usual way, was gathering momentum on the doorstep, he was hurried into the parlour. Hurried I knew it was, if not in time, at least in a flight of mental processes, both in my case and as I guessed in Dalethwaite's; and a prolonged and vigorous scraping of boots did not lessen the impression. He entered, hat in hand. His accustomed shyness fell from him like a cloak as he came through the doorway, and was forgotten, as though the big smile were for the moment the only physical effort of which he was capable.

"Well, Aa nivver!"—and the ejaculation smothered the greeting on my own lips. "Well, Aa nivver!" he repeated as he came forward with a long stride to take the hand outstretched to him.

I was sorry I had told him to put his hat down. It caused unexpected difficulties. He didn't know where to put it, and the problem bothered him; but presently it was satisfactorily solved by his sitting down in the proffered chair and depositing the hat immediately beside his feet. The disposal of the hands created a further and unforeseen embarrassment, not perhaps so much because they were without tools and without a hat-brim to twitch the fingers round, as from the fact of their betraying the work he had just left. He looked from them to me with the comical expression of a boy caught blackhanded, and made furtive efforts to hide both them and his own discomfiture, now suddenly increased by the appearance of the lady of the house. He looked immeasurably unhappy. Here clearly was a case of a bull to take by the horns.

" Well, Dalethwaite, here I am still useless in dressing-gown and slippers, and you busy as ever. Is it stake-cutting, well-building, or "—I added a little maliciously—" or perhaps banking-up that bridge?" The chance shot relieved the situation. A smile half-astonishment and half-whimsy spread over his face, as he exclaimed:

" Mans! hooivver did you knaw? You've hit it, sartin. Oot of woods isn't oot of mind, then? But Aa nivver doobted it. . . . Aa should have dipt 'em as Aa came alang. Aa nivver thought ayder to be seeing you." He had resumed the subject mechanic-ally, for surely it no longer held any terrors for him. He was full now of me, of my recovery, of the woods, the ardours and renewals, and all the bracing allure-ments of companionship—and of the sandpipers. That first whustle had come to him when he was delving far within the wood—" there might have been naw sic thing as a sandpiper for aw Aa was thinking of it "—and every day subsequently he had gone night and morning the whole length of the shore from Great Bay to Water-lily Bay to count the arrivals, twelve pairs up to date.

" Aa've tried to reach the baker's dozen—maist ivver Aa've knawn—but it's naw good. And Aa doobt naw more'll come noo. Aa was puzzl't with

counting nows and thans—they're a bit skifty yet—
but Aa couldn't mak mair than twelve."

"Not in school-hours, Dalethwaite?" I queried.
It was impossible to resist the temptation the
furrowed face offered by its quick and naked response
to every stimulus, the sudden alertness strung to
every key of wonder and enquiry, at first wrought
with such seriousness as to reproach the inciting
word, and then, as usually befell, dissolving into the
most willing and generous of smiles. It was so now.
He turned towards the lady of the house, and said
laughingly:

"Aa don't think Aa'm called on to keep school-
hours at my time of life." Then slipping back into
reminiscence, he added, "Aa don't think Aa ivver
did, yan time or t'oder."

I don't suppose he ever did; and perhaps that
was the reason he was the man he was.

I plied him with questions, covering the many
weeks that had passed, and recaptured bit by bit the
story of the woods. He told me what the storms
had done; of the breach in the wall made by a
blown Scotch fir—"and hoo that oot-at-t'elbas
dogger't bit of a wind week afwore last ivver came
to doon sic a bonny tree" he couldn't conceive; of
flooded paths and the clearing out of runners; of his
new fences and still mounting pile of stakes; for to
this festival day his contribution was a willingness to

talk, a greater willingness to smile, and, either as a consequence of his own pleasure or of his wish to foster mine, a more active foray than I had ever known him indulge in Cumberland speech.

The subject of the oak stakes, being oak, kindled him to excitement. He went on: " Knoppy as these hands o' mine " (he spread them on his knees, the soiled palms downward), " and for the seamm reason, mappen—oot in aw winds and weathers, and a match for them aw. Though Aa'm not saying it doan't pull 'em oot o' shape a bit. Naw knots, and where would your oaak be wid aw the trooncings and yarkings he gits? But he's straight enough at the heart. Nivver saw a grain to beat that tree—when you got deep enough. Aa could na find it in my heart to use sich for stakes. Aa just kept to the boughs and snags—plenty of 'em for my job, and tough work too. That's where the kongy timber was—ootside—a leand from the storms; t'oder close knit and straight in ivvry grain. . . ." Here he paused and fell into the mood I had so often remarked in him as liable to come at the end of some longer effort, when his head, as now, sank a little lower on to his chest, his face grown serious as though intent on things of greater moment, and with a lowered voice he went on: " Ay, straight enough there; aw the hay-bay, come what will, nivver turning a grain on't, and grawing and tightning ivvry year."

Preparing to go——and it was a process of some length——Dalethwaite turned to the lady of the house and said, " You'll have him weall for the bird-nesting? " I hastened to reassure him, and added an enquiry after the squirrels. His face fell.

" Those raggelt of lads, the rapscallions! they've bin at 'em o' Sunday marnings. Aa wish Aa had 'em, t'heall lot, and a good ash stick in t'oder hand."

" Like an Emperor of Rome who wished his subjects had but one neck, eh? " I ventured.

He laughed: he laughed heartily.

" Ay, ay! Yan trouser-seat amang 'em! There'd be no mearr trouble in Brandley if Aa could lay ower it, ayder."

" But he was a terrible villain, that Emperor, Dalethwaite."

" Well, Aa've naething to say aboot emperors or aboot necks. Mebbe he didn't mean it. Trouser-seats and those randies, a plague on 'em! are anoder matter when there's squirrels in it."

I agreed.

IV

During the conversation I had broached the subject of a visit to his cottage. If there was a quiet glance of surprise on his face, there was a more lasting and more convincing look of pleasure. He assured me I should be right welcome, the lady too. Day, hour, and meal all came under cheerful review. Dalethwaite entered into the question as though something big were at stake. In the triangular rally of queries, suggestions, answers, withdrawals, that showed perhaps an element of perplexity as well as of mutual interest, he did from time to time unmistakably knit, however slightly, those deep shaggy brows, as one who would say, not so much " I am thinking," as " I am doubting." But the knitting was so speedily unravelled, and so cleanly, there could be no doubt it expressed no more than an idle fancy. The day was to be the first sunny day I could walk so far; a Sunday, because Dalethwaite would be at home without warning; afternoon, and as early as we would, to ensure a good rest, refreshment, and a walk back before nightfall.

The opportunity came sooner than we had anticipated because of a sudden turn, not of weather merely, but of season. " The spring comes slowly up this way," but it keeps to rule as waywardly here as elsewhere. The leap was of that record-breaking order not unusual in England, and in one kind or another, and while heart and limb are sound, the final triumph, if not always the most acceptable, of the English climate. Preparation had long been going on in the ding-dong fashion of March and early April—half-gales and gentle breezes, squalls of hail, rain, snow, days " rayder slattery," winds that swept the earth dry in twenty-four hours, and again days of unclouded sunshine. These laſt, along with more genial airs, had been ſteadily and quietly winning ground of late, and the dale was ready for the change. A day of northerly bluſter and brief spurts of hail towards the end of the week had seemed to defer the promise, but it proved an idle threat and served only to heighten the effeƈt of a viƈtorious contraſt.

Viƈtory was complete and this ·time permanent. The greyness of earlier hours had gradually thinned out and left the sky cloudless, but not the cloudless-ness of mid-summer with its theatre-at-noon effeƈts, as Coleridge described them. But the light we call golden, the light of autumn mornings and evenings, drenched the valley from end to end, from a sun half-hidden in its own luminous haze among the diſtant fells: while the ridges and prominences of the fells nearer and on either hand, widening out as they approached, were thruſt into this same mellow light, their recesses filled with deep umber shadows, cut here and there by the silver of watercourses that seemed to intrude a spirit of reſtlessness and triviality on a scene so large and peaceful. Here and there too escarpments of rock gleamed after recent rains, gleamed and flashed as the sun smote them, and faded again into the sombre hues round about.

When the woods were reached we turned from the road into the narrow path we ourselves had worn

on our almost daily errands to the village. Whether
it was shorter than by the road no one ever seriously
wished to know, or wished long enough, though the
question was discussed from our first to our last
using it. We had thrashed the matter out—to
everyone's satisfaction, but to no one's conviction;
we laughed over and dismissed it, each pluming
himself on the finality of the opinion last delivered.
We did everything but measure it. Sometimes,
returning at nightfall after a long day on the fells,
when the last mile counts heavily, I should have
been glad enough to have known with certainty; but
on the morrow, the pleasant path, the discussion
beginning and ending in jibes and laughter, and
fruitful for other days, my own travail of the night
before unimpressive to others and now visionary as
a dream to myself—all these things proved, what in
our hearts we knew very surely, that the question
was not one to be settled in this transitory life.

Though we had worn the path we had not been
the first to trace it. That had been done, as the
making of paths through woods and meadows ever
should be done, by children on the way to and from
school—in this case by two boys, sturdy, shy, and
rosy-cheeked, our neighbours across the bay. In
this choice of path-makers there was surely the hand
of Providence—or at any rate I made out a case for
Providence in discussions not less heatedly contested

203

than the question of length, with Nine-year-old and Five-year-old, and still more heatedly when they were Ten and Six. Had it been left to girls, would the path ever have been made? I protested my faith that girls in a wood would keep to the road, but protest died before the adventurous spirit it strove against. I was surer of my ground on the second count, countervailing judgment was less sure, and divided: namely, whether if girls had made it, it would have been the path we knew, the crooked, merry, mazy path that struck full into the face of every projecting slab of rock, that drove clean through every bog, whereon boulders had been dropped at sorry intervals to serve as stepping-stones, and that took as many curves and as many dips and hummocks as ingenuity could discover before it returned to the road within the last step of the wicket-gate. I did not suggest anything so improper to the ears of youth, but we elders all know that

The rolling English drunkard made the rolling English road.

Is it less certain that schoolboys, and only schoolboys, and only on the way to and from school, could possibly have contrived such a madcap, loitering, mischievous track as those young urchins, our neighbours, had made, and we, easy victims of temptation, had beaten, with certain exaggerations, into a well-worn path?

Stillness was in the woods as we passed through, the stillness that accords so well and yet so mysteriously with conflicts of light and shadow, with the birth-throes of great trees and the million things underfoot—the urgent thrust of life everywhere. In the more sheltered places we caught glimpses of budding larch, glimpses of the more modest green of elders, honeysuckle and bramble, and of some more adventurous branch of chestnut, ever willing to court disaster for the sake of an untimely and vain display. Elsewhere the portents were less evident, no more indeed than a heightening of the colour that lingers throughout winter in woods far removed from the smoke of towns. But for this, oak, ash, and silver birch seemed to be sleeping out their deep winter sleep.

We had remembrance of previous years to guide us to a hundred happy re-discoveries by the way— the sunken glade one had to step aside from the path to look into, and there the white-starred anemones were already out, and the bluebells coming; favourite peeps won at a venture long ago; trails of Dale-thwaite and his unsleeping winter in shored-up paths, palisades and repaired walls, seats and bridges well and truly set for the summer visitor he loved not; the long winding lane between woods and village, at every turn of it the jaws of the dale opening wider to reveal in due time the clustered green-roofed cottages with the smoke of wood fires drifting lazily across them, and Glaramara in the distance—the one fell of them all that weaves a garment of beauty out of whatever atmosphere—and the still more distant summits of Great End and The Pike. All these on a Sabbath day's journey to take tea with Peter Dalethwaite!

V

At the bridge that spans the river and low-lying land between the village and coach road, we sat for a while looking into the deep pool, into which the trout glided from the current swirling alongside it, leaving its own surface without a ripple—one of them a wondrous fat fellow disporting himself as though this were his unquestioned domain, and those others but momentary intruders; such an one as every angler, since angling became a subject for conversation, has hooked, and lost, and told the weight of to credulous listeners. Too comfortable to bestir himself? So it seemed through many a minute of watching; just a well-fed, corpulent, contented soul, of all species a type peculiar to fishes and men for whom the gods fetch and carry, and from whom nothing is asked but to receive. He gave pleasure too, this old trout in his quiet pool, just by the staggering and imperturbable complacency of his demeanour within earshot and the throb of all that hurrying life of water fresh from the hills. At intervals he opened his mouth—that way came acceptance; once only he switched his tail, and settled down into a position of new comfort. We could not see that the gods asked more of him but only to thrive thus and thus.

The last stage was the valley road, its own turns and dips and the windings of the river bringing them ever and anon together, so close below us that we could look down into more pools basined in green stone, interrupted by shallows, over which the waters broke into countless eddies of merriment. The river-bed and clear water were alike beautiful in their setting, which comprised every feature one could desire or name for an English mountain stream, the reaches differing in many measures of length and width, and terminated by every shape of curve; closed in by deep glistening rocks or opening between low sunlit meadows; overhung here by a solitary silver birch, there tunnelling through such dense masses of tree and undergrowth that the path must leave the bank and make a wide detour before again joining it. . . .

It was all familiar as the face of a friend, and such familiarity, if it be close enough, draws within its scope both what is usual and expected and those momentary surprises that time and circumstance inevitably bring about, though the precise nature of them cannot be foreseen. We are prepared for a change, and our guesses may be as nearly prophetic as affection can make them; but when the moment of proof comes, the change is already part of the old order of things. It is only the changes of disease, of injury—of death—that will not be reconciled. In them the order is broken, familiarity a ruined scroll. Nowhere are moods and their expression so many, so rapid, so unexpected, so beautiful as in these districts of high mountains and heavy rainfalls; and among these, Cumberland and Westmoreland achieve beyond all others because their fells are more numerous, more varied in form and character, and, since they lie within so small expanse, more rich in composition. But, as Dalethwaite says, " You maun leave the roadds—roadds are for carts and cattle and trippers—if you want to knaw. Climb; and at ivvry step something happening and garn to happen." He is right: it is height and toil that reveal the glory in full measure. But even in the dales you get hints of it as you tramp along, while to these far off is added the dale's own contribution of things nearer at hand, more homely, and more intimate. And change here, too, is on the great scale—" naw two days ivver alike," as Dalethwaite commented out of long experience half an hour later, in almost the first words spoken after the business of welcome had been got over. It was not on this day or any other, merely or chiefly the transformation of season; it was the effect of light, of shadow, of colour, varying with every hour of the sun's progress and with all the inconstancies of wind, cloud, and haze. And to-day's expression, changes, readjustments, new to us though they were, only strengthened our sense of an old and unbroken intimacy.

CHAPTER NINE: DALETHWAITE AT HOME

There are for every heart certain words which are nearer or more akin than any others; and often in some remote . . . out-of-the-way place, in some lonely nook, we unexpectedly meet a man whose warming discourse makes us forget the hardships of the road . . . and the contemporary world, full of the follies of mankind, and of deceptions that cloud man's vision; and an evening spent in that manner remains with us for ever.

GOGOL

I

TO the wayfarer Dalethwaite's cottage was a conspicuous object from afar off, and this not so much because of its elevated situation or its architectural features, though to the discerning eye these gave it a favoured distinction, as from the fact that once it had attracted his notice it would vanish and reappear, draw nearer and withdraw again into the distance, with a capriciousness neither usual nor reasonable in a human habitation. A traveller looks for stability in his landmark, and from the traveller's point of view this was the one quality lacking it. Perhaps for this very reason it was the more likely to engage his attention or excite his curiosity. His hopes, if he had hopes of an inspection at close quarters as a reward for the pranks it had played him at every stage of his progress, were doomed in the end to disappointment. After his first clear view of it, a turn in the road, a dip, then many another turn, threw a succession of obstacles between the pedestrian and the cottage, until at last, when it reappeared, he knew that every step was now taking him farther away. He had not even recognized the approach to it—how should he when the approach gave not a single Christian evidence of its existence? According to the mood in which disappointment found him he might at the backward glance decide whether he were the more impressed by the frivolous treatment to which this cottage, in appearance humble and demure like other dale cottages, had subjected him, or by its deep and mysterious withdrawal from the life, such as it was, of the road and neighbouring village.

Its secret was kept to the very last, and nowhere so closely as at the point of departure from the highway. To leave the beaten path when you will and in whatever direction you will is so much a rule of the dale that the discreet in making choice will only consult their inclinations, and in exercising it only have a care to close gates after them and to avoid injuring fences, walls, and crops. Obedient to this rule you may plunge at any moment into the unknown. Before a mile is passed you may encounter difficulties—there are many as the names of Allah, and not even a camel knows the last of them; but there again if you have discretion you will know how to evade them; if you lack it, then may you find compensation in endless possibilities of discomfiture and merriment.

Such an adventure, so far as signs were concerned, might have been our sole purpose when we abruptly turned from the road that afternoon. The village lay in the distance, but except for the roofs and walls showing in vague green patches between trees and hummocks of rock and heather, there was not a trace of human habitation in sight. Yes, one, at last! Over the steep mound fronting us and over the larch that clung to its sides, a column of blue smoke rose in delicate spirals against the sombre background of fell. " There! " we exclaimed in one voice, as eagerly as though the proximity of a cottage, a rest, and refreshment were the things nearest our desire.

In our haste we scrambled up the mound rather than spend needless time circuiting it, to discover in the worn ledges and polished stones a track long used to the stress of feet ascending and descending. This rude stairway, with its almost unmanageable intervals from step to step, was clearly the approach to home of a man in haste to be there at full stride— " naw zig-zags or twists, or nonsense of that sort aboot it." Mounting in his wake, brief as the toil was, I had no breath to spare for conversation or laughter, though there was food for both in dogging the old man in his own difficult footsteps, and himself the quarry awaiting us over the other side.

Straggling and abundant heather stretched away in every direction, with the rust of winter still on it, and there in the midst, and much nearer than we had anticipated, stood the cottage, saturated with sunshine, sunshine over its white gleaming walls, sunshine in such plenty on its few meagre diamond-paned windows that they gave it back in streams and jets of reinforced lustre. In spite of this adventitious appearance of cheerfulness, the poverty of window-space, the amplitude of blank wall, and the severe neglect of all architectural fripperies, gave it an air of cloistered and frugal simplicity, like the choice and the announcement of one who, whatever his work in the world, desired to spend his leisure in his own way, aside from it. Yet this impression was corrected by one of compelling geniality. It looked, not so much a cottage exposed like other cottages to an indiscriminate share of sunshine, as one sunning itself for sheer pleasure. Nor this alone. Its recently whitewashed walls, its green door and casements, its ordered flower-beds, grass-plot, palisade, gave a smile so friendly, so human, that one would have felt no surprise if children had come running out laughing and shouting a welcome. A narrow well-beaten path, closed over in places by the deep heather, ran towards the entrance in as nearly a straight line as the irregularities of the ground allowed. Farther along emerged a continuous pile of stones, evidently the ruins of a former wall, which, as it neared the cottage, had been rebuilt to form, with the help of a massive boulder deposited there in bygone ages, one boundary to the garden. From the boulder swung a rough-hewn oak gate, unpainted as oak should be and as I guessed polished in due season with oil, and flanking it on the other side was a solidly square-built pier of stone. " Dalethwaite all over it," I said; and it occurred to me how often on this walk the same thought had come to me.

We passed through into the enclosure. A path of stone-chippings went direct as an arrow to the house—and here again " naw nonsense aboot twists and twirls," to use a phrase infinitely varied with which Dalethwaite dismissed many subjects beside paths;—on either side of it a narrow herbaceous border, and beyond these plots of grass close up to the boundary, the larger of them interrupted by a circular bed of rose bushes. Roses of the sturdy briar type, honeysuckle, and cotoneaster covered the walls and palisading; roses, clematis, and cotoneaster, the last carefully trimmed to circle a window, climbed about the front of the cottage, though without marked resolution, as though the victims either of undue exposure or of a conscience stricken by the exceeding whiteness of the surface provided for them. Chintz curtains decorated with pink roses, luxuriant leaf, and wonderfully thorned and convoluted in stem, but now beneficently more than a little faded, hung from the lower windows.

As I looked at them while we stood waiting on the doorstep, a momentary uneasiness seized me. Their prim party look betrayed a suggestion of ceremonial I could not associate with Dalethwaite, and which, if it were present, would cloud our visit and colour I know not how much of our future intercourse. They had the unmistakable look of having been washed, ironed, and groomed for a state occasion. I recollected, too, Dalethwaite's own rather ceremonious addiction to order and primness, to the shyness moreover that does not easily break through the show of things even when these belie what lies beneath. And still no sign from within; no sign of life but the blue smoke, no longer sweeping upwards with steady assurance, but only a blur, shapeless, lambent, and capricious, against the sky. Was our host lost in the affairs of preparation, or these completed was he perhaps resolving the formularies he judged appropriate to the occasion? He must have heard the scrunch of gravel as we came up the path and our voices in unsubdued conversation at his very door.

How quickly in moments of apprehension, trivial even as this, pictures flash across the mind, and as quickly give place to others all shaped to some dominant thought, recognized or not. The sight of those curtains prompted them. At one moment I saw Dalethwaite standing, where he had been standing any time the last half hour, ready in a trice to answer the knock that was so slow in coming; at the next, merely busying himself for our comfort: or again pacing to and fro over the stone floor, his brow puckered, his hand driving hurriedly through a more and more flustered shock of hair. A knock would settle the matter, and was indeed overdue. I knocked. The rat-tat on a door not quite rigidly held gave unexpected reverberations. The sound started a rush of new emotion, sweeping away former impressions, former scruples. Before I realized what I was doing my hand had lifted the latch, and as the door swung open I shouted a greeting.

Immediately within was the large kitchen-parlour in which I had so recently spent the night, beyond it was another smaller kitchen or scullery, entered by a door partially open, through which could be seen a rude stone sink, two rows of saucepans and other culinary vessels, and an amorphous shape, swathed in linen, hanging from a hook in the ceiling. From the farther room, after a moment's silence, a voice, speaking more to itself than in answer to my challenge, exclaimed in a tone in which pleasure did not altogether conceal surprise and embarrassment: " Well, Aa nivver! "—and following a rattle of crockery out strode Dalethwaite.

His face was a study as he came towards us. A greeting was on his lips, in his precipitate movements, but it seemed to be entangled and unable to free itself. He turned sharply to one side, fixing his eyes, his whole being, on the grandfather clock away beyond the fireplace. " Aa'm douced! " he said. . . . " Aa've forgotten to wind him up." " He " had run down, how long before I don't know, for Peter did not recognize Greenwich time.

II

The thing was on his mind. He conquered it to the extent of settling us comfortably in chairs by the log-fire, and then resolutely set himself to convince us by words and gesture that a trivial discomfiture must not be allowed to arrest the stream of hospitality. But the effort was as apparent as the result, and kept pace with it, cheek by jowl. The grandfather clock was the mute shadow over all. Its immemorial tick silenced, it spoke with another voice, and poor Dalethwaite's conscience was the sole instrument on earth designed to receive and transmit the message. To us, like spectators at a séance, it was only given to look on sufficiently impressed without appearing to pry too closely or to rush in where mediums fear to tread. Perhaps the error in the time had frustrated schemes hatching in the back room at the very moment of our arrival, schemes nicely planned and matured, on the successful execution of which depended a host's reputation.

I believe that no one, not the sphinx himself, could keep a secret reposed in him better than Dalethwaite; his own half-secrets such as the child evolves and the child's consuming enjoyment in is to reveal, he could no more keep than a child. I knew the premonitory signs—they were as clearly to be read in that daylight face of his as print—and waited. This three-cornered prattling was mere subterfuge and dilly-dallying. I knew it, and Dalethwaite knew it. There was the uneasiness of guilt written in every line of his face, in his every inconsequent nudge of conversation, though it passed in a twinkle when I chanced to arrest the furtive glance to and from the clock. I still waited. At length:

" Aa can't think hoo it came aboot," he began with great deliberation. " Aa wind him as regular as— as clock-work . . . ivvry Saturday on the laſt ſtroke of five—juſt afwore Aa have tea, and the hole's clear." Before it was possible to commiserate he turned to the lady of the house, and resumed as to his chosen confessor:

" Aa was juſt cutting a slice or two of bread for buttered toaſt, to have it fresh, you knaw." . . . He was again at an impasse. The predicament offered at leaſt two solutions, but his native hue of resolution was so sicklied o'er with the pale caſt of thought that he couldn't persuade himself to suggeſt the obvious one.

" Bring it out, Peter! Out with your skeleton

218

from the cupboard!" I broke in. "Of all jolly occupations in a cosy cottage parlour the jolliest is making toast for tea over a glowing log-fire."

Dalethwaite strode off in high glee. Dalethwaite's stride was one of the first traits I had remarked in him, and it was one of the most characteristic—"Yan that suits me doon to the ground, Aa suppose," he assented, laughing contentedly at his witticism, when one day we chanced to be talking about it. It was the stride you noticed whenever you saw Dalethwaite in motion. It needed no getting-up of steam to set it going; here within these narrow walls as out on the pack-road, it went full-swing from the first moment. We had encountered its exactions and penalties on ordinary folk mounting the steps on the hillock only a few minutes before. Dalethwaite never knew that I had taken actual measure of it, but I had, and the measure was a good thirty-four inches. We have all remarked in some busy thoroughfare the man barging along at thirty-four inches to the stride. Sometimes we have written him down an ass, sometimes upon closer acquaintance we have named him less equivocally; but always we have felt the man himself a gawk, and his gait ungainly and a little ridiculous, a caprice of boyhood fossilized into a habit. With Dalethwaite it was far otherwise: the stride was the man. You could no more disassociate his stride from Dalethwaite than the backward poise of wing from the Nike of Samothrace, or his sloping shoulders from Lord Balfour. It had kept pace with the man's own growth, with his stature of mind and character no less than with his development of limb, and it was all compact of strength, determination, zest, geniality, and willingness. In a word, an abundant stride, the like of which for grace and sufficiency I have never seen in a man before or since.

He returned, triumphantly armed with two forks, one designed for the purpose—what might be described as a parish toasting-fork, massive and formidable; the other, pressed into temporary service from other uses, he insisted on keeping for himself. The lady of the house, contrary to her instincts and all known experience, was left to watch and comment. Between him and me Dalethwaite set a mounded plate of bread, cut in rounds—and " naw nonsense aboot that " either!

We set to work. A delectable task in sooth, and one drawing straight from the springs of conviviality. No ice comes down from that source. We chatted merrily, and laughed together. The lambent flames pursued each other swiftly from a core almost too dazzling for the eyes to look into, yet crowded with magical shapes of things if one looked steadily enough, leapt from log to log, and vanished into the gloom of the chimney.

Dalethwaite kneeled on one knee, his shoulders bent forward over the other, his head thrown a little back, exactly in the attitude I had so often watched unknown to him, when, rod in hand, he fished for trout from the lake-shore. The very novelty of his attire was no disguise, least of all a caricature. Shining broad-cloth from head to foot, polished boots, a collar white and starched as the window-curtains, a grey tie of ample dimensions flopping widely over a closely buttoned waistcoat—all strange indeed, all the occasion for a momentary surprise on a figure never before seen in other than rough well-worn homespun. I watched him bowed over his toasting, this old woodman in the unaccustomed garb of gentility, the hair carefully brushed that had always before been teased out by wind or fingers, the glancing firelight, now that the room was growing more dim, insistent on the fullest display of both man and clothing; and yet nothing was at fault, nothing incongruous, nothing for amusement or challenge, and least of all for regret. He was become simply the Dalethwaite of the Sabbath and of home.

The pile of bread decreased rapidly as one slice after another was passed on steaming to the lady of the house (the title Dalethwaite always gave to her) to be buttered. My own share in the task had become mechanical. I was watching Dalethwaite—or rather brooding dreamily over the thoughts that gathered about him. The glare of the fire, the delicious warmth, the languorousness of the occupation following the fatiguing walk, had partially overcome me with drowsiness. Silence had fallen upon us all. It was now growing dusk. The bowed figure on the other side of the hearth was as Rembrandt would have chosen—broad knobby forehead, bushy eyebrows, big shapely nose and sensitive wide nostrils, bearded mouth and chin, in the depths of which couched exceeding gentleness and exceeding strength; and I was looking on it, and looking on the ruddy light that spread like a nimbus over the face and silvered hair, and faded abruptly into the black clothes—and even these things I saw as in a dream.

" Mans alive! "—and before I realized where the alarm lay Dalethwaite had drawn my toasting-fork to one side, and with ejaculation and laughter was showing me the blackened piece of toast at the end of it. I had repeated the sin of King Alfred, and perhaps with as good an excuse.

We drew our chairs round the table. Such viands as were not already there, our host carried in with an air of great satisfaction and import from the inner room. The pastry-cook of the village had been raided for our benefit. A bowing acquaintance, already effected by the children, gave me a clue to the genera, as dish after dish was spread before us;

but not always to the variations, which seemed to show a sudden and bewildering access of cross-fertilization. A plate of girdle-cakes, hot from another fire, unctuous and wonderfully browned, were the contribution of Mrs. Blencowe, Dalethwaite's nearest neighbour, friend, and stand-by, and later for some few years his housekeeper. Plates and dishes, like Joseph's coat, of many colours were spread over a tablecloth so lavishly starched that its creases rose defiantly whenever they escaped the burden of them. The tea-service was an heirloom, remembered we were told from earliest childhood, gay to frivolity with sprigs of roses and forget-me-nots tied with streamers of pink ribbon. There was honey in the comb from Dalethwaite's own hives. In the centre of the table stood a flattish glazed bowl, lidded and very blue, set in metal filigree, and sprawling wide on metal legs. Its own challenge to notice was reinforced by the solicitude our host displayed towards the contents, which he pressed upon us with something of the eagerness of the vendor of quack medicines, as an alternative to honey in the honeycomb. Curiosity overcame settled conviction, and before we knew it, before the most cursory investigation, the die was cast, morally at least, and we had subscribed allegiance to the blue bowl. It contained raspberry jam, fragrant, pellucid, shimmering like other well-ordered raspberry jam, but comprised of the tiniest fruit surely ever used for such a purpose.

No effort was needed to invite its story. Dalethwaite was deep in the mood to traffic with any subject that turned up. On his face was one big smile and many twinkles. He was waiting upon our wants before we wanted, in the spirit more of festivity than of a calculated hospitality. He was alive and quickened as I had never before seen him, like the forest oak when the wind goes through it. He became positively and increasingly garrulous, though one had to encourage the stream discreetly now and then and to take care to leave the pauses to Dalethwaite's own disposal.

III

" That raspberry preserve? Aa'll tell you heall aboot it." He chuckled. " You'd nivver believe it. Aa ought to begin by rights, ' Yance upon a time,' for that's hoo it did begin," and dropping his voice in the way so habitual with him, that gave by contrast an expression of withdrawal to distances remote and unshared, he added, " And Aa guess it'll not be lang afwore it ends. . . . Aa was a lad aboot twelve or thirteen, living with my oald grandam. Aa must have given the oald woman a seet of trouble in those days. Aa was a boy ivvry inch of me, alang wid oder boys; yet betimes Aa was aleann—Aa was happiest

mebbe then—leaſtways, Aa can beſt call to mind the
haver-skaverings Aa was up to aleann. Noa great
harm in them, you knaw, but they worrited the oald
woman. Aa think she was puzzl't too—could
nivver get to the bottom of them. Naw wonder; I
couldn't myself. Aa did ivvry mischief but go
bathing in the lake "—(here he gave a sly look at
me)—" Aa couldn't at noa time bring myself to that.
Trees and rocks Aa scrambled up like a monkey,
for nothing but devilment; though I don't recolleƈt
the going up, mind you, so much as two or three
times coming doon. . . . Poor oald woman, Aa can
see her scaared face noo, me all tattered and bleeding,
ey, yance worse than bleeding. Well, well! . . .

"Maiſt of all Aa liked to go aff and away to the
fells—played truant Aa doobt betimes. Yance Aa
made a neet of it—without meaning to, you'll
underſtand. Such a chang as nivver was! T'heall
village turned oot to search. And that was the only
time Aa was ivver scaared in my life—not at getting
loſt, hooivver, not a touch, but at getting foond.
Aa'd slept gradeley in the deep heather, when Aa
could get to sleep for looking at the ſtars. They
were all roond me, in and oot, gone and back ageann,
dancing and glenting among the twigs ower my headd.
It was the seamm wid the dew when its sparkles woke
me in the morning, millions of them, like drips from
the sun.

"Weel, Aa roosed myself and set off as fast as my legs would go, till Aa came to a beck splashing doon a bit of rock; and though doobtless Aa was as backards at washing as most callants, Aa was soon on my knees sousing my face ower and ower ageann, and then staying to watch the bubbles break through my fingers, and forgetting aw aboot heamm. Suddenly Aa heard voices ahint, and then—dear, dear!—yan headd after anoder tipped up ower the brow from nowhere, oald Plaskett, Jim Applethet, Measter Thursby from the *Dale Head*, Slee, and Aa don't knaw who not—aw in such a skufter as nivver was. . . . Oald Plaskett was for rozzelling me there and then. 'Nay,' said Measter Thursby, 'let the young gad-ageatt aleann, he's done no wrang, leastways not to thee. Why, man, thou'dst nivver have seen a night of stars or got an appetite for breakfast but for him.' That was a crack at Plaskett—a kamp't, ketty make of a man, ower fond of the bar at the *Dale Head*, and too much tak up wid his legs maist neets, Aa doobt, to see much of stars. . . .'"

Dalethwaite stopped with a snap, like a lid closing on a box, till presently he resumed in another tone, intently:

"That was the first time Aa ivver began sorting people oot. Aa hadn't given it a thought afwore that moment. Some knawing aboot things, slow to anger; some t'oder kind."

"Sheep and goats," I suggested. He turned to me with a puzzled enquiring air.

"Naw. Aa see nothing much to choose between sheep and goats; they're both poor widdering feckless things, naw good whativver except for what's on them. Wid folk its different: Aa don't reckon *them* much good except for what's in them. Oald Plaskett was for using his stick. A man must use something when he's cornered, and Aa guess he'd nothing else to use. Just butting like sheep and goats, for the seamm reason. Aa'd nivver had a walloping, and Aa don't knaw that Aa wanted to begin then. But, mind you, that wasn't what Aa was thinking aboot."

"You felt the injustice and stupidity?"

"Yes, that's it—stupidity. But it's something else. There's nobbet horns and claws and hoofs to some folk, and nothing ahint to hold them. If you're in their roadd, doon ye go, whether it's butt or kick. . . . Aa'd nivver given the oald mischief a thought till then. Aa knawed he'd a hank o' gangan oot at neet—not ower the fells, ayder. Aa knawed oder things—his own children had a sight of things to teall aboot him; but Aa'd nivver come up ageann it till that morning. It wakened me up mair than the sousing Aa'd just had in the beck."

"You'd eaten of the fruit, like Adam in the Garden, Peter."

227

"Ay, that's truth.... And the taste nivver left me."

"You must take the rind with the flesh," I volunteered sententiously. "It's a choice fruit, is knowledge, but it often comes bitter to the tongue." He was so bemused that I don't know if he heard the platitude; but, after a longish silence, during which I had turned to gaze into the fire, thinking my own thoughts, he added very deliberately:

"Ay, ay ... and the more you knaw the less you sleep."

"Peter, I believe you're right." And then in the long pause some lines occurred to me, then in manuscript, and I went on: "A friend of mine, a poet, must have felt just the same when he wrote:

> But men at whiles are sober
> And think by fits and starts,
> And if they think, they fasten
> Their hands upon their hearts.

IV

It was high time to turn the subject. A sadness was brooding over the old man's face I had never before seen. It well became him, but in its shadow he suddenly seemed old.

"Well, Peter," I broke in, laughingly, "you've indulged us in a most spacious feast—from raspberry jam to the fruit of the Tree of Knowledge!"

"Well Aa nivver! Those raspberries, to be sure!

Aa'd clean forgotten all aboot the raspberries. If Aa'm not pecking and glopping aroond like an oald hen! The fact is——"

"The fact is, Peter, you're a born story-teller. Shall I tell you something I have discovered in life? Every man is two men; caged in this vile body there are always two of us. In some cases each is quite distinct and separate from the other. Number One may be a big, burly, domineering fellow, and leave scarce elbow-room for Number Two, who may spend most of his days crouching about in any hole or corner of the tenement till his opportunity comes to pop out for an airing. And a fine mess he may make of it when he does! If by chance they meet it is probable they will cut one another, or condescend to a stiff recognition like two men in the smoking-room of a London club. In some again they are boon companions; they are not happy or at ease out of each other's sight a single five minutes. Their devotion is so uncritical, their sympathy so complete, that they positively grow alike in countenance, in traits, in all outward appearances. They express the same thoughts and feelings, nod approval of each other all day long, laugh the same laugh for just the same number of seconds, smile, cross their legs, blow their noses just in the same way, and I expect kneel side by side and repeat nightly the same prayer in the same voice. You can no more tell one

from the other than Tweedledum from Tweedledee.
You go to call; Number One lets you in, relieves
you of hat and coat, conducts you into his sanctum.
Thrilling! You have got him alone at last. Not a
bit of it. Just as secretively as Eve came forth from
the side of Adam, and the Garden was suddenly and
wonderfully peopled no longer by the man only, but
by the man and the woman—as if it had been no
otherwise from all eternity, and so must remain to
all eternity: there, in unquestionable shape, is the
other fellow, summoned to the presence the moment
initial formality is over and the business of the visit
begins. On goes the talk, grave or gay, between you
(but remember there are two of you also, though you
may be like the first two I named, and one of you
may have been left behind)—on goes the talk between
you and your hosts, but you can't always be sure
which of them is listening or which of them is turning
your words over in his mind; least of all can you be
positive which of the two it is that replies, unless you
are quick to notice some little inconsistency or some
unexpected phrase or opinion, or to perceive some
expression, some curl of the lip, some attitude of legs,
movement of hands, modulation of laugh, that is for
a fleeting moment unshared before the other is swift
to recognize his cue and follow suit. The trouble
comes when these two fellows, merged so thoroughly
into one, are, if one sees deep enough, profoundly

different in spirit, in soul, and are only forced into
marriage, as it were, by the gods for their own amusement and for the undoing of one more excellent piece
of manhood. For instance, the poet and the actor,
the novelist and the shopwalker, the painter and the
confectioner, the statesman and the mud-lark, or—
the woodman and the story-teller," I added slyly.

Dalethwaite, whose perplexity meanwhile had
deepened as in a man beset by invisible and unascer-
tained assailants, broke at this last proof of benignity
into a broad smile of relief and satisfaction. He
seemed indeed hugely pleased. Had I at a venture
pierced through the man's homespun—his daily
wear—to a hidden core of vanity? Or was it perhaps
with Dalethwaite, close on seventy, as it was with
Mr. Pepys in the late twenties, when, as he confesses
about some trifling incident or other, " I was, as I am
at all new things, very much joyed "? He had
doubtless never known himself the subject of serious
discussion before. Possibly he enjoyed the experience merely of having his name mentioned in a select
company; or was it that he derived a heightened
pleasure in finding gifts recognized of which he
himself was dimly conscious and secretly emulous,
and of which he had, unknown to himself till that
moment, regretted the long and enforced disuse?
Who knows? He smiled the smile of an expansive
and novel contentment.

And I believe it was never so tasted in other place what maner a thynge the sweete conversation is that is occasioned of an amyable and lovynge companye.
HOBY's *The Courtier*

Not Heaven itself upon the past has power
But what has been has been, and I have had my hour.
DRYDEN

I

"YES, Peter," I went on, " the dale knows you are a woodman, and I know you are the teller of tales. In olden days you would, following your bent, have wandered from village to village, from castle to monastery, with a harp slung over your shoulder, chanting proud stories of knightly heroism, love, war, of beautiful maidens, of favours and troth-plights, of wizardries, of the tournay and the chase."

I paused to enjoy the effect my words had quite unexpectedly made. The old man's eyes were fastened on me, except for a momentary glance toward the lady of the house, given as though to make sure, not so much of her sharing the enjoyment as of satisfying his own mind by visual corroboration that the room he sat in was really his own snug parlour, that there was the tea-party in full swing for which he had been preparing so literally, and that in point of fact he was not at that moment disgracing the occasion by standing on his head.

232

The wide and rapid transition of emotions made a demand on Dalethwaite's facial expression to which it can rarely have been subjected. To them all it made an immediate and faithful response, like one of our sheltered mountain tarns that alike reveals its own depths and reflects the objects around and over it, till a puff of wind comes, now from one quarter, now from another, and the surface is a moment ruffled, then grows very still again and the broken images are restored. Dalethwaite looked at me so fixedly, with such wonder, incredulousness, hilarity, satisfaction, questioning, that I could but go on.

" You would likely enough never have felled a tree," I continued, " never built a dry wall nor cleared a runner. You might never have set eyes on these fells, unless perhaps in your wanderings you had descried them from far off, as blue clouds on the distant horizon, and of no deeper concern to you. And if by chance you had come hither, come to this very dale, how your mediaeval lowland soul would have turned askance from their bigness, loneliness, ' horridness,' fitting, you would think, the northern churls—the dalesman, your forefathers, sturdy, silent, clean living—they closed in by their high imprisoning walls from all that made life good and merry and plenteous. You look surprised, but even a short hundred years ago that opinion was commonly held, and there are people living to-day who would

consider life in the dale banishment and the fells the
abomination of desolation. Do you know, Peter,
I often talk to a man, a motor-car driver, not five
miles away, who says: 'Fells? Beauty?—fiddle-
sticks! I'd like to see 'em all rolled out flat. This
country ain't fit for car or Christian. Give me the
Brighton Parade or the Great North Road—
whe-ew!' and the face that had at first positively
glowered with malice shone ecstatically at the very
mention of those two names, as though they were his
signed discharge from purgatory to paradise. And
your crowded hour of glorious life would probably
have befallen tramping that same Great North Road
on the way from castle to monastery, from fair and
festival to the dining-halls of robber-chiefs and king-
makers. But the woodman in your blood would
always have been a disturbing presence, calling you
to the woods as an English spring calls the swallow.
You would hear in many a lonely moment the words
of the old Gaelic song drumming in your head:
'My hope and my love, we will go for awhile into
the wood, scattering the dew, where we will see the
trout, we will see the blackbird on its nest; the deer
and the buck calling, the little bird that is sweetest
singing on the branches; the cuckoo on the top of
the fresh green; and death will never come near us
for ever in the sweet wood.'

"I picture you, Peter," I continued, " in the New

Forest, in Sherwood, twanging your harp and telling wonderful tales to Robin Hood and his merry men, keeping over-late hours with Friar Tuck—at no saintly offices, I fear me—and away next morning at the dawn to more serious affairs. And left to yourself you would begin thinking things over, merrily at first, for the joy of the morning would be in them; but all the while they were spiriting you away to a subject that would never be long put out of mind—unless it were in the company of the Friar Tucks—and one that was growing more and more difficult to escape. . . . You are swinging along over the wet grass, careless of paths; the sun has just risen above the trees, and you feel the sudden warmth of his greeting, how good it is—a hail and God-speed to all who go afoot honestly; the birds know no harm of an intruder, and sing as they sang to Adam, and to Chaucer on a certain April morning, the song of creation. You push aside a briar, carefully, for the rose is on it, and come unexpectedly on an open glade, sloping upward towards a thicket of trees in deep shadow. There you stand, not counting the minutes, motionless and irresolute. It is not that you are uncertain in which direction to go, or trouble much now or at any time to seek paths other than men have made—you prefer, unless time is pressing, to follow your own. It is something else that holds you, some trouble of mind that has replaced the joy

235

and confidence of this June morning. The pleasant glade suddenly opening at your feet, with its patches of light and shadow, challenge you to answer here and now the question you have so long put by. It asks, in words you have lightly turned over and dismissed scores of times before: 'Listen, you teller of stories. Is all the story-telling in all the halls of Christendom worth this, this gift I keep for you?' This time, you feel, it is a struggle to the death, a struggle between combatants every fighter of them closer to you than your dearest friend. You are no mere onlooker either. No concession here possible to the vestige of the cloven hoof in you, in the craven reflection that come what will your own precious hoard of life is secure from hurt. It is your own heart that takes every thrust. If only there were a sound of trumpets, war-cries, of clanging weapons to fire your blood! There isn't. The struggle goes on in deathly silence, and you share it as the dreamer shares the pitiless torment of a nightmare. . . . Suddenly a stag breaks out of the thicket; he sees you, and halts a moment in a splendid poise of irresolution and alertness, when the winding of a horn comes from the distance and he bounds forward over the wet green sward towards the woods, and is lost to sight. The conflict within you is not quite ended, and it will be renewed many a time hereafter, but thanks to the intrusion of the stag it has grown more

desultory and you can survey it with something of
the impartiality of an onlooker. You continue your
journey all that day, and the next day until evening,
sometimes by road, but this only when you are no
longer a free agent or when the attractions of town
or village, with their welcome and their flatteries,
prove too seductive a venture. Truth to tell, you
have lost a good round number of miles both days
by staying to gossip by the way, for like another
great story-teller who confessed, ' With an out-of-
doors labourer or an old woman gathering sticks
I can crack for ever,' you are conscienceless in luring
ploughman and harvester, forester, tinker, monk on
ambling pad, maiden going a-courting, anyone and
everyone of the countryside, into idle converse.
There was once a wise man, Peter, who bade those
who had half an hour to spare not to go spend it
with those who hadn't—golden advice, too, but to
you as story-teller and vagrant, to your victims
perhaps also, a rule not to be thought on.

" Well, by the evening of the second day, you have
reached the castle. At a blast from your horn the
drawbridge is let down and you pass over, welcomed
by porter and steward, the latter of whom conducts
you into the presence. The baron-chief, his knights
and ladies, sit at high table in the great banqueting
hall; retainers on rude benches alongside two oaken
tables running down the middle of the floor, side by

side. It is a strange scene to come upon at the end of a June evening, straight from the quiet woodland and quiet sky. The flare of torches, stirred by the cooler air from without, is no constant light, but sways about the room like the water splashes among the bays and headlands under a press of wind, suddenly irradiating one group and now another of swarthy grim-visaged men, clad in garments of many dusky colours, belted and cut skirt-like down to bare knees, and throwing immense impenetrable shadows into the timbered roof overhead. There is an air of expectancy over the throng. A clamour of voices and of constantly shifting attitudes, of boots and benches scraping on the stone floor, of weapons clanging, resounds through the hall; while eyes rove restlessly towards the entrance and turn back again as muttered words pass from lip to lip. At length the great door swings on its hinges, and you, Peter the Rhymer, stride in. You are ushered up to the high table, set in a place of honour, given to drink in turn from a deep flagon that is passed round to every man by his neighbour, and served by waiting-men to incredible helpings ·of beef, venison, and capon; and then——

> When they had ete, and grace sayd,
> And ye tabyll away was leyd,
> Up aroos Ypomydon.

That's you, Peter—Ypomydon—the story-teller;

and the night is yours! You will be a woodman another day. But first of all else you are the artist—one rôle at a time, and your whole heart in it, whatever the hours of secret conflict that are experienced between. . . . Now tell us about the raspberries."

II

Dalethwaite required a few moments to readjust himself.

"Aa nivver!" he at length remarked with a significant respiratory effort—"Who's the storyteller noo? Weel, weel! you've left me seah Aa hardly knaw where Aa am, like a bat moyder't in broad daylight. It was not seah strange nowder while you talked, no mair than a dream o' neets while you're dreaming."

"You felt the cap fitted, Peter."

"Naw, not noo Aa'm wakened up. Umph! Aa don't knaw—it's a rum an, hooivver—though it was summat-like when you were garn alang. The seamm as the light on the fells—the light can make anything of them, and meakk you believe anything. Aa knaw them backards and forrards; they're just tossed up into ivvry sort of shape and covered ower wid bents and heather, and Aa reckon that's aw they are to some folk. There's Threlkelt, poor dowly, sleddering fellow! he nivver knawed they were for anything but grazing sheep. It's being wid sheep,

239

Aa doobt, that does the mischief. . . . But it's anoder story looking up at them, and you keep on looking. . . . Ay, that's it—a story—Aa guess that's the lang and short of it. You teakk me and meakk me into a story, leaving enough of me to meakk no mistake. And it's the seamm wid the light when it has a mind to go story-telling aboot the fells."

"That raspberry jam, Peter." He laughed heartily.

"Well, you will have it, Aa see; but you've fairly taken the wind oot of my sails. And it's not much of a story after aw. There are naw birling harps, nor stags breakking through covert, nor banqueting-halls. It's nobbet a tale of a little chap going twelve or thirteen who ought to have been at school, and wasn't. . . . Ey, now Aa come to think on, my story starts off t'seamm as yours. Seamm trouble bothered both of them, the man coming sudden on the glade and the young truant. There was something got at them. It's happened afwore—two masters, and it's one or t'oder, or a mess-up. Your man sounds aw reet, but he's in a havy-skavy, and he'll get deeper in, wid·aw his story-telling and fine feasts. The lad knawed a trick worth two of that and gave t'heall trouble a clean pair of heels. . . .

"Aa was gangen alang the road, lontering and poking in and oot, when Aa happen't to look up at Scrammel Brow. Aa knawed it as weel as Aa knawed my own hand, but Aa'd nivver seen it like that afore, nivver. Aa'd nivver heard of anyone going up it, but aff Aa went.

"You'll understand, it was a morning early in August—yan of those dog-days that go lapping up the mist as fast as ivver they can. The sun was far behint, not a glent on the fell-face, though it wimpl't and glister't in the air afore it, like a curtain, ay, a curtain through which you could see a sight of things you could nivver have seen withoot it; and amang them Aa believed Aa could see a way up. Weel, there 'twas—Scrammel Brow was no more oot of my reach than an apple orchard, seah Aa thought. But Aa saw things that weren't there—a mistake Aa've made once or twice sin."

He paused and guffawed lustily as though he were recapturing the spirit, not the memory only, of an auspicious boyish adventure. In all Dalethwaite's longer efforts there was a singular temptation to join in. It was a good game to watch, but one seemed to be missing some of the fun. But in this case it was high time to get to the raspberries, and a chance remark, however well intentioned, might draw a red herring across the trail; I therefore left him to fill his pause undisturbed.

"Ey, 'twas good enough, to be sure," he broke away again, "though it's been better since Aa used my headd, and an older headd to it; in those days it was legs or nothing. Mans! have you ivver watched the ants when you've tumbl't their nest ower? Weel, that's hoo Aa first scrambl't up that Brow. There were ledges and snags and screes in pleanty, but it was a ladder with mair gaps than rungs. Hooivver, Aa hadn't gone far afwore Aa knawed there was nothing for it but to go on; gangan back would have been quicker, but Aa reckoned Aa shouldn't knaw much after the journey got started. Seah on Aa went, hoisting myself on to a knee, swinging roond yan snag after anoder, clinging on to clumps of fern and heather that gave way, till at last Aa came to a pitch that baffl't me. It was siven or eight foot straight up; Aa might be able to scramble it if the tufts of grass and a knob or two of bowder held tight, but if there was naw ledge on the top Aa was done. That bit of a bank Aa'd have jumped doon wid a heart as light as a blawn leaf, came ower me as big as death. It pull't me together too, for instead of butting at it like a bull, as Aa'd been doing t'heall way up, Aa turned it ivvry inch aboot, back and edge. But it was aw questions and naw answers, t'seamm as looking into a grave. . . .

"Aa tried a hoald here, a hoald there; yan tuft tore off like paper, then anoder; oot came a bowder and fetched a slither of rubble wid it. Hoo lang Aa doan't knaw, but for langer than Aa've ivver knawn, ayder afwore or since, my feelings were churning too thick to see through 'em. Aa couldn't see the ladder for the steps! For what wid the tumbl't stones and my scratching aroond, a lot of holes had been made, and making anoder or two as Aa went up would let me on to the top. . . .

" Come and gone, it was no more than a puff, but it was aboot as lang, was that siven foot climb, as t'heall of my life afwore."

He stopped abruptly. I think he was going to add something about that seven foot as a measure also of death, but he bethought him and looked at us in turn with close scrutiny, and smiled and shook his head, as though reproaching himself for a narrative unduly harrowing. His low muttering voice towards the end and his own intent preoccupation in the recital had certainly given it a touch of tragedy, but comic relief came in the next breath when he broke forth:

" And noo Aa've almaist got to the raspberries! There was no mair balancing on yan leg like a herensew, no more doldrums; Aa jumped as far and landed as safe as Jonah when the fish spew't him on to dree land. The fell towered up on ayder side like geatt-posts to remind me of what Aa'd been through—but what does it matter aboot geatt-posts when you're yance inside them? The roadd to heaven may be a terrible lang climb—Aa don't knaw; leastways it's often enough a seet of pain and trouble packing-up and getting off; but Aa

reckon you drop aw the baggage you've brought
wid you at the door. Aa'd carried a deal that day,
but it tumbl't away the moment Aa landed in yonder
gap and lay sprawling on aw-fours on a bed of soft
mossy turf. Aa'd hardly time to tak it aw in. The
gap went winding and climbing till it opened oot
on to the fell-top, and Aa could hear a trickle of
watter birling doon. Aa couldn't see it, 'twas hidden
so deep in fern, and crockelty bur, and steep, blue
buttons, thimble, bull toppins, codlins and cream,
horse nops, booin, and Aa don't knaw what. But the
birling was enough, and Aa was up and aff like a
pop-gun. Winje!—Whativver . . .? Aa couldn't
believe my own eyes——"

" What, raspberries? "

" Nae, we haven't got to the raspberries yet," he
answered mischievously. " You'd nivver guess to
the end of days. . . ." The pause was sufficiently long
to accept the challenge had there been one. There
was no interrogation in his voice—he didn't intend
it. He was hugging the notion of a delighted secret,
his sole concern to prepare a quick and virgin soil
for its reception. Almost he was disposed, at the
call of an ejaculation only used on joyous occasions,
to a betrayal of the dale's dedicated rule of deliberate
utterance; in truth he was hurrying his words pre-
cipitatively, but they still lagged far behind the eager
pace set by voice and gesture. The abruptness of the

silence was like the breathless moment of runners nearing the goal. Ypomydon knew his business.

"White heather!" he burst out—"not a sprig, mind you, nor two sprigs, but a heall clump as big roond as my two arms! And, lo and beholt, a six-foot aff, anoder clump bigger than t'oder. You hear talk of being frightened oot of your skin—that's just aboot hoo Aa was stagger't. Aa was fair slew't! The flower-garden aw roond, blue and white and yellow, filled the slip of dale like flowers in a basket. Aa doobt if any eye had ivver lookt on them befwore and likely none sin except mine—unless, mebbe, Threlkelt's, though there was nothing there of any use either to Threlkelt or his sheep. Ivvrything else, perches and poles of them, was raspberries," he ended with perverse suddenness.

"But what about this jam? You filled your greedy stomach, I know, and I suspect your every empty pocket as well; but the supply hasn't held out fifty years."

"Aa've not missed gangin'," he replied quietly, "scarce yan single year sin. Aa get the scramble, but Aa don't always get the preserve. That's a bit like the rest of life. Sometimes it's July, maistly August, nows and thans September, according to the season; but aboot yan year in fwore they nivver ripen, just shrivel or moulder aff. My oald granny, God bless her! meadd the preserve ivvry year, 'twas

245

the last thing ivver she did. Poor oald soul, she had scarce strength left to stir the pan, but she would keep hobbling from her chair to go and flutter the spoon aboot. But Aa saw well enough—Aa saw hoo 'twas. Her een follæt me roond close as a cat watches a mouse. Whativver Aa did they follæt, but she was watching me mair than anything Aa was ageatt on. Aa watched her too, and gabbled a lot of stuffment atween whiles—as Aa used to whistle garn alang on dark neets when Aa was a little chap. But Aa knawed that nothing Aa said had anything to do wid what she was looking. When the jars were put safe away she said, ' It'll last you langer than afwore, Peter. Aa think Aa'll be gangan to bed.' Ey, and she nivver got up oot of it, nivver spoke anoder word, though she lived two or three days langer."

III

After many protestations, of word and gesture, against our helping in the rather extensive work of clearing the tea things away, the old man was won over, even to the extent of making merry at our dark and untutored efforts; but no amount of persuasion would induce him to let us share in the washing-up. Our boggling, where it occurred, was not due to ignorance of general principles or to lack of experience in the genial art of " siding away," but rather to

our host's punctilious obedience to the settled regula-
tions of his own house and his concern in exacting
the same of other people. The demand went to the
extent of tyranny; it embraced the letter, and every
letter to the last possible, whatever the fruitfulness of
the spirit. Moreover, if ever Dalethwaite indulged
the mood that so unfailingly came under his castiga-
tion in others, and displayed irritability or ill-humour,
it was when you were giving him assistance he did
not want and using methods and effecting results he
did not approve. If you had the courage, or perhaps
only the understanding to adopt the measure, your
sure road to redress was quite firmly and quietly to
tell him, in the word learned of his own lips, that he
was " kanjy "—though for lasting results it might
be wisest merely to withdraw your help as though
nothing had happened. I knew my man. Had I
not watched him marvellously trimming and apportioning blocks of stone that would in their final
position never again be seen; pointing stakes with
the utmost nicety for consignment to earth; building
and rebuilding his wood-stack, dragging out a log
here, patting another in there, possessed solely with
the intent of sightliness and order, even though the
morrow would necessitate disarrangement and some
portion of the task being done over again? And
Dalethwaite of the woods and work-days no more
allowed the uses of hospitality to gloss over his native

fibre, or colour his rooted habit, than Sunday clothes to taint his customary demeanour.

Yet, I suppose, it is every man's experience that characteristics that are more or less fluid in the outer world are precipitated, as it were, and crystallized in one's own home; or perhaps the narrower field of operations subjects them, like a microscope, to sudden and surprising magnification. Dalethwaite was under the lens, this trait of orderliness exposed under the highest power and for periods long and frequent enough to provide details of a picture now mellowed by time, in which, because of them, he becomes so much more vivid and companionable a memory.

I recollect, for instance, that when the washing-up was done he returned from the scullery carrying in his hand a tangle of knotted string. At great labour he unravelled it, untied every knot, and then carefully wound it round his fingers, secured the loop, and crossed the room to deposit it into an oak salt-box hanging beside the window. This done he carried each chair used at the table to its appointed place against the walls, not after the fashion of most householders, but rather like a curator arranging his specimens in the case. And so on, to the extent of a dozen trifling acts seriously, even slavishly, executed as a ritual. One felt that the creak of a chair under one's careless strain, or dropping one's cigarette ash

on to the carpet would have made Dalethwaite sorely
uncomfortable. But of the many varieties of angels
in the house, ministering or otherwise, this one of
orderliness only reproaches if we court rebuke, and
only offends if the beating of her wings, when it
should be no more than " almost heard," insists on
brushing against us like a bat, ruffling our hair, or
tweaking our noses, in pursuing its own feverish ends.
In Dalethwaite the foible was manifested so naively
and withal so unobtrusively as to afford only amusement—yea, and something beside, for one would
have hastened to add, in a phrase worn to the comfortable uses of friendship, " and so like him."

But once the " siding away " was done, in the
woods or here in his own house, the old woodman
lapsed into a serenity more deep, more cloistral than
I have ever known a man of his energy and eager
temperament to acquire. As an appanage of old age
it usually expresses mere apathy. In Dalethwaite it
was a positive not a negative quality, something
added unto him, intimate, pervasive, significant. A
straight-backed chair gave it an increased impressiveness. " Early Victorian," I thought as I looked at
him strenuously puffing clouds of bluish smoke along
the stem of a blackened pipe, the bowl too fuming
and crenulated at the lip, like the crater of a volcano
—but not in the sense in which it has been too long
and slavishly fashionable to use the phrase; for as I

watched him, erect and deeply bemused, the finely shaped head, the blue searching eyes, the strong sensitive lines of nose and mouth, brought to my mind visions of a great age more vivid and still more heroic by the spectacle of this man who lived in a remote English dale, and had lived as he would die only a woodman, unknown and soon unremembered.

IV

Evening had fallen, and we talked on in desultory fashion, looking into the fire, and rarely of a mind, so it seemed, to look away from it. During his first pipe Dalethwaite had got up to light the lamp; he had left the curtains undrawn for the sake of the " last blenk of day," as he expressed it, held to the last in the rude diamond-shaped panes. The time was drawing near for departure. Indeed, the subject had already more than once been mentioned, but it floated away and disappeared as inconsequently as a leaf on the wind. For some long while, I recollect, the only concern of vital importance in the room seemed to be the leaping flame of the log fire. Conversation became a mere blowing of bubbles that thinned and vanished as they took shape; till presently there was no other sound save the clock ticking and Dalethwaite pulling fitfully at his pipe.

Suddenly he rose, crossed over the room to the window and drew the curtains. " The only time

Aa don't want windows," he explained, settling down again in his chair and throwing another log on the fire, " is when they've grawn shiny black. Aa don't knaw whether Aa'm afeart of seeing things Aa nivver have seen and don't rightly believe there's oot of the sort; but a glisky window-pane when it's dark always tealls me, kind of whispering, a lot of things Aa don't particularly want to hear aboot."

" You mean you don't like the dark? "

He looked from one to the other as though to make quite sure of his ground.

" Naw, Aa doan't," he replied with emphasis—" at leaſt, it's nayder yan thing nor t'oder—it's mair of a hummel-jummel than Aa ivver feel aboot anything else."

" You, Peter?—you actually upset by darkness? " He laughed a little uneasily.

" Ey, you're surprised and naw wonder. It's the rummeſt tangle Aa knaw. Aa can't even laugh it ſtreatt—mebbe because Aa can't laugh hearty enough. If your own laugh won't settle you comfortable in daylight you can't expect it to settle the things that come at you in the dark."

He lifted his pipe from his knee, where it had been lying after determined and fruitless efforts at re-lighting, and jammed it into the fartheſt corner of his mouth with an almoſt savage energy. I could hear his teeth clench it. He lowered his head and gazed abstractedly into the fire, the eyelids raised as though peering over spectacles—and in the familiar figure before me I saw with wonder the likeness, in attitude, feature, and expression to his great namesake in Madox Brown's picture. He needed prompting if the subject were to be continued, but for many minutes I was too intent on the resemblance, and too occupied with the excitement of watching it grow more and more close as his head fell still lower on to his chest and the lines on the forehead became more furrowed, to wish the spell broken. Even the presence of the pipe hardly affected it, or seemed an irreverence. The mouth pulled to one side, drawing the lips tense, and puckering the cheek in a deep fold round the pipe-stem, did not caricature the other, but only showed him, as it were, in another phase, more homely, more in the light of common day, but still brooding and perplexed over high matters.

A movement on Dalethwaite's part destroyed the picture. He looked quietly towards me, and with his changed attitude and expression we easily fell to renewal of the old subject.

"Tell me, Peter," I began—"I am really interested. Do you mean that you are—not actually afraid, but uncomfortable out of doors in the dark?"

Laconic as he could be, indeed as he invariably was in casual acquaintance, I noticed how increasingly with us, and more than ever on intimate occasions like the present one, he avoided direct and categorical replies. In this I feel convinced he was betraying, under genial conditions, the disposition natural to him. He enjoyed self-expression; he enjoyed unpacking thoughts and memories that had long been put away, and turning them over to the light and air. Such storage was the practice of the dale, and he had fallen into it, not from a miserly instinct, but because only the vain and flippant expose their goods in the sight of those who will display none. He was enjoying the experience now, as he went on:

" Aa can make nowder back nor edge of it. Ivvrything is inside oot—voices, and you doan't hear them, sights, and you doan't see them. Footsteps coming up behint you, and nivver a soond—overtaking you, but they won't come alangside, least of aw gang aheadd and have done wid it—some dropping doon to your own pace, and dogging you t'heall road; oders blustering up like a rush of wind, and there's no mair to it than just a bit of a shiver ower you. It's worst when they come hunting in couples," he added with great seriousness. " But it's aw fleuterment. There's naw one there, and yan minute you knaw there's no one and the next you doan't. And you ca' yourself the biggist fule you can find a neamm for, and you knaw you deserve it, but you can't say it strang enough to be certain. . . . They aren't aw

coming on foot ayder——the air's a bit thick sometimes, behint. Nows and thans Aa look roond and
give a bit of a laugh. It's like blawing at a dandelion
clock——nothing of it left after you've blawn——and Aa
have the night aw to myself till they're back ageann.
But maistly Aa think, ' Hoots! Aa won't turn my
head for the heall lot of you! ' and Aa keep to it, but
it does naw good, whativver. When Aa was a callant
Aa was nigh scared oot of my life; it's only rayder
worriting now——breakks your peace, like neighbours
dropping in when you want maist to be aleann."

" Where does the black window-pane come
in? "

" It's the seamm wid the black window-pane," he
replied simply, and threw another log on the fire.

Again we discussed departure, and again after
bestirring ourselves in initial preparations we settled
back in our chairs, drawing them nearer to the fire.
We now touched on a variety of subjects, mostly
trivial affairs of the dale, past and present woven into
one fabric like woof and weft, or of Dalethwaite's
own childhood. It was he talked, as we wished and
schemed it, but the talk was, in the few minutes left,
no more than a series of jerks and ventures, like a
crackling of thorns under the pot. Names were
mentioned, and men and women of importance in
their day, but now long dead and forgotten, lived
again for a moment in Dalethwaite's story. He

254

referred to many incidents of childhood, to escapades easy enough to associate with boys in general, but presenting at the other end of the telescope, as Dalethwaite himself directed it, a bundle of impishness too shapeless and tattered for recognition—the first, and, as he confessed, the most daring of them, his own advent into the world, on a winter's night, wild and so full of snow that neither doctor nor midwife could be obtained, the attempt even to secure a neighbour half a mile off having nearly cost his father his life. These things he told us, however abruptly, with unmistakable relish, like a man celebrating an occasion with a vintage wine that has acquired the bouquet and dignity of long cellarage.

We got up, this time with serious intent to leave. Thoughts of the recent conversation floating unconsciously through my mind directed my eyes towards the window. A pallid hue, unlike the warm dim light of the room, spread over the curtains, paling its scarlet roses and green leaves, and overflowed its border like a diaphanous fringe; the gloom beyond deepened to almost total darkness by the meeting of many shadows, to which our own figures and the furniture of the room contributed.

" Spite of your drawn curtain, Peter, there's a face looking in to-night."

" Ey," he laughed. " Aa don't see t'oders, or hear them, when there's a moon, be it nobbut a slip o' yan. But it's aw fleuterment, aw an oald man's babble. . . . You'll have a grand walk heamm."

As we bade good-bye the lady of the house made one of those remarks, such as only a woman can make, that sum up all the pleasure enjoyed and all the pathos—the regrets, deprivations, wistfulness—that ever lurks somewhere on its outskirts, when, catching her whole meaning, Dalethwaite said to her smilingly:

" Aa'm nivver lonely, you knaw, and maistly Aa've got the company Aa like beasst—and naw end to it," he added with a look and laugh that rather betrayed his previous statement. " But Aa've nivver been seah crowded befwore as to-night. You'll come ageann, besure? Good-night to you! good-night! "

Printed in Great Britain by Lowe & Brydone (Printers) Ltd., London, N.W.1

A LIST OF THE

VOLUMES NOW PUBLISHED

IN THE

TRAVELLERS' LIBRARY

3s. 6d. net
each

JONATHAN CAPE
AND WILLIAM HEINEMANN
LONDON

THE
TRAVELLERS' LIBRARY

A series of books in all branches of literature designed for the pocket, or for the small house where shelf space is scarce. Though the volumes measure only 7 inches by 4¾ inches, the page is arranged so that the margins are not unreasonably curtailed nor legibility sacrificed. The books are of a uniform thickness irrespective of the number of pages, and the paper, specially manufactured for the series, is remarkably opaque, even when it is thinnest.

A semi-flexible form of binding has been adopted, as a safeguard against the damage inevitably associated with hasty packing. The cloth is an attractive shade of blue and has the title and author's name stamped in gold on the back.

A NOTE
ON THE ARRANGEMENT OF
THIS CATALOGUE

The main body or text of this list is arranged alphabetically under the names of AUTHORS. But, in addition, and for the convenience of readers, there will be found at the end two indexes. The first (page 31) is arranged numerically under the series numbers given to the volumes. The second (page 35) is arranged alphabetically under the titles of the books.

ANDERSON, Sherwood

HORSES AND MEN. Stories   *No.* 54

'*Horses and Men* confirms our indebtedness to the publishers who
are introducing his work here. It has a unity beyond that of its
constant Middle West setting. A man of poetic vision, with an
intimate knowledge of particular conditions of life, here looks out
upon a world that seems singularly material only because he
unflinchingly accepts its actualities.' *Morning Post*

ARMSTRONG, Martin

THE BAZAAR. Stories   *No.* 77

'These stories have considerable range of subject, but in general
they are stay-at-home tales, depicting cloistered lives and delicate,
finely fibred minds. . . . Mr. Armstrong writes beautifully.'
Nation and Athenæum

ATKINS, J. B.

SIDE SHOWS. Essays. With an introduction by JAMES
BONE   *No.* 78

Mr. J. B. Atkins was war correspondent in four wars, the London
editor of a great English paper, then Paris correspondent of
another, and latterly the editor of the *Spectator*. His subjects in
Side Shows are briefly London and the sea.

BELLOC, Hilaire

SHORT TALKS WITH THE DEAD   *No.* 79

In these essays Mr. Belloc attains his usual high level of pungent
and witty writing. The subjects vary widely and include an
imaginary talk with the spirits of Charles I, the barber of Louis
XIV, and Napoleon, Venice, fakes, eclipses, Byron, and the
famous dissertation on the Nordic Man.

BERCOVICI, Konrad

BETWEEN EARTH AND SKY. Stories of Gipsies.
With an Introduction by A. E. COPPARD   *No.* 117

Konrad Bercovici, through his own association with gipsies,
together with a magical intuition of their lives, is able to give us
some unforgettable pictures of those wanderers who, having no
home anywhere, are at home everywhere.

BIERCE, Ambrose

CAN SUCH THINGS BE ? Stories   *No.* 1

'Bierce never wastes a word, never coins a too startling phrase ; he secures his final effect, a cold thrill of fear, by a simple, yet subtle, realism. No anthology of short stories, limited to a score or so, would be complete without an example of his unique artistry.' *Morning Post*

THE EYES OF THE PANTHER. Stories   *No.* 49

It is said that these tales were originally rejected by virtually every publisher in the country. Bierce was a strange man ; in 1914, at the age of seventy-one, he set out for Mexico and has never been heard of since. His stories are as strange as his life, but this volume shows him as a master of his art.

THE MONK AND THE HANGMAN'S DAUGHTER.
Written by Ambrose Bierce in collaboration with Adolphe
   Danziger de Castro   *No.* 34

'They are stories which the discerning are certain to welcome. They are evidence of very unusual powers, and when once they have been read the reader will feel himself impelled to dig out more from the same pen.' *Westminster Gazette*

BIRRELL, Augustine

MORE OBITER DICTA   *No.* 140

'A volume delightful to read, packed with urbane and shrewd criticism, and distinguished by a pleasant vein of kindly humour.' *Daily Mail*
'Age has not wearied Mr. Birrell's humour ; nor have the years condemned his whimsicality. He remains as delightful a companion as ever.' *Nation and Athenæum*

BOURNE, George

A FARMER'S LIFE   *No.* 32

The life-story of a tenant-farmer of fifty years ago in which the author of *The Bettesworth Book* and *The Memoirs of a Surrey Labourer* draws on his memory for a picture of the everyday life of his immediate forbears, the Smiths, farmers and handicraft men, who lived and died on the border of Surrey and Hampshire.

4

BRAMAH, Ernest
THE WALLET OF KAI LUNG — *No. 18*

'Something worth doing and done. . . . It was a thing intended, wrought out, completed and established. Therefore it was destined to endure, and, what is more important, it was a success.' *Hilaire Belloc*

KAI LUNG'S GOLDEN HOURS — *No. 16*

'It is worthy of its forerunner. There is the same plan, exactitude, working-out and achievement ; and therefore complete satisfaction in the reading.' *From the Preface by* HILAIRE BELLOC

BRONTË, Emily
WUTHERING HEIGHTS — *No. 30*

'It is a very great book. You may read this grim story of lost and thwarted human creatures on a moor at any age and come under its sway.' *From the Introduction by* ROSE MACAULAY

BROWNE, Louis
THE STORY OF THE JEWS — *No. 146*

Here is a history which is more absorbing than any work of fiction. The author traces the beginnings of the Jewish race from the wandering Semitic races of Arabia, through interminable strife and conflict, slavery, oppression, expatriation, up to modern times.

BUTLER, Samuel
EREWHON. A Satire — *No. 11*

'To lash the age, to ridicule vain pretension, to expose hypocrisy, to deride humbug in education, politics and religion, are tasks beyond most men's powers ; but occasionally, very occasionally, a bit of genuine satire secures for itself more than a passing nod of recognition. *Erewhon* is such a satire. . . . The best of its kind since *Gulliver's Travels*.' *Augustine Birrell*

EREWHON REVISITED. A Satire — *No. 12*

'He waged a sleepless war with the mental torpor of the prosperous, complacent England around him ; a Swift with the soul of music in him, and completely sane ; a liberator of humanity operating with the wit and malice and coolness of Mephistopheles.' *Manchester Guardian*

BUTLER, Samuel

THE NOTE BOOKS
No. 75

'To us Butler stands not chiefly as a satirist or an amateur in fiction or in the fine arts, but as the freest, most original and most varied thinker of his generation. . . . Neither *Erewhon* nor *The Way of All Flesh*, but the posthumous work entitled *Note Books* will stand, in our judgment, as the decisive contribution of Samuel Butler to the thought of his age.' *Nation*

SELECTED ESSAYS. This volume contains the following essays :
No 55

THE HUMOUR OF HOMER
QUIS DESIDERIO . . . ?
RAMBLINGS IN CHEAPSIDE
THE AUNT, THE NIECES, AND
    THE DOG

HOW TO MAKE THE BEST OF LIFE
THE SANCTUARY OF MONTRIGONE
A MEDIEVAL GIRLS' SCHOOL
ART IN THE VALLEY OF SAAS
THOUGHT AND LANGUAGE

THE WAY OF ALL FLESH. A Novel
No. 10

'It drives one almost to despair of English Literature when one sees so extraordinary a study of English life as Butler's posthumous *Way of All Flesh* making so little impression. Really, the English do not deserve to have great men.' *George Bernard Shaw*

CANOT, Theodore

MEMOIRS OF A SLAVE TRADER. Set down by
BRANTZ MAYER and now edited by A. W. LAWRENCE   *No. 126*

In 1854 a cosmopolitan adventurer, who knew Africa at the worst period of its history, dictated this sardonic account of piracy and mutiny, of battles with warships or rival traders, and of the fantastic lives of European and half-caste slavers on the West Coast.

CARDUS, Neville

DAYS IN THE SUN : A Cricketer's Book
No. 121

The author says 'the intention of this book is modest – it should be taken as a rather freely compiled journal of happy experiences which have come my way on our cricket fields.'

CARLETON, Captain George

MILITARY MEMOIRS (1672–1713). Edited by

A. W. LAWRENCE   *No.* 134

> A cheerful sidelight on the war of the Spanish Succession, with a remarkable literary history. Johnson praised the book, Scott edited it, and then the critics declared it to be fiction and suggested Defoe or Swift as the author ; now it has come into its own again as one of the most vivid records of a soldier's actual experiences.

CLEMENTS, Rex

A GIPSY OF THE HORN. Life in a deep-sea sailing ship   *No.* 136

> A true and spirited account of a phase of sea-life now passing, if not passed, fascinating from the very vividness and sincerity of its telling. Mr. Clements loves the sea, and he makes his readers love it.

COPPARD, A. E.

ADAM AND EVE AND PINCH ME. Stories   *No.* 13

> Mr. Coppard's implicit theme is the closeness of the spiritual world to the material ; the strange, communicative sympathy which strikes through two temperaments and suddenly makes them one. He deals with those sudden impulses under which secrecy is broken down for a moment, and personality revealed as under a flash of spiritual lightning.

CLORINDA WALKS IN HEAVEN. Stories   *No.* 22

> 'Genius is a hard-ridden word, and has been put by critics at many puny ditches, but Mr. Coppard sets up a fence worthy of its mettle. He shows that in hands like his the English language is as alive as ever, and that there are still infinite possibilities in the short story.' *Outlook*

FISHMONGER'S FIDDLE. Stories   *No.* 130

> 'In definite colour and solid strength his work suggests that of the old Dutch Masters. Mr. Coppard is a born story-teller.' *Times Literary Supplement*

THE BLACK DOG. Stories   *No.* 2

> 'Mr. Coppard is a born story-teller. The book is filled with a variety of delightful stuff : no one who is interested in good writing in general, and good short stories in particular, should miss it.' *Spectator*

COYLE, Kathleen

LIV. A Novel. With an Introduction by REBECCA WEST
No. 87

'*Liv* is a short novel, but more subtly suggesting beauty and movement than many a longer book. Liv is a young Norwegian girl whose father is recently dead. She is engaged, half against her will, to a young man, a neighbour ; but she desires above all things to go to Paris to "see life." . . . There is something cool and rare about this story ; the reader finds himself turning back to re-read pages that must not be forgotten.' *Times Literary Supplement*

DAVIES, W. H.

THE AUTOBIOGRAPHY OF A SUPER-TRAMP.
With a Preface by G. BERNARD SHAW
No. 3

Printed as it was written, it is worth reading for its literary style alone. The author tells us with inimitable quiet modesty of how he begged and stole his way across America and through England and Wales until his travelling days were cut short by losing his right foot while attempting to 'jump' a train.

LATER DAYS. A pendant to *The Autobiography of a Super-Tramp*
No. 48

'The self-portrait is given with disarming, mysterious, and baffling directness, and the writing has the same disarmingness and simpleness.' *Observer*

A POET'S PILGRIMAGE
No. 56

A Poet's Pilgrimage recounts the author's impressions of his native Wales on his return after many years' absence. He tells of a walking tour during which he stayed in cheap rooms and ate in the small wayside inns. The result is a vivid picture of the Welsh people, the towns and countryside.

DELEDDA, GRAZIA

THE MOTHER. A Novel. With an Introduction by D. H. LAWRENCE. (Awarded the Nobel Prize 1928.)
No. 105

An unusual book, both in its story and its setting in a remote Sardinian hill village, half civilised and superstitious. The action of the story takes place so rapidly and the actual drama is so inter-woven with the mental conflict, and all so forced by circumstances, that it is almost Greek in its simple and inevitable tragedy.

DE MAUPASSANT

STORIES. Translated by ELIZABETH MARTINDALE   *No.* 37

'His "story" engrosses the non-critical, it holds the critical too at the first reading. . . . That is the real test of art, and it is because of the inobtrusiveness of this workmanship, that for once the critic and the reader may join hands without awaiting the verdict of posterity.' *From the Introduction by* FORD MADOX FORD

DE SELINCOURT, Hugh

THE CRICKET MATCH. A Story   *No.* 108

Through the medium of a cricket match the author endeavours to give a glimpse of life in a Sussex village. First we have a bird's-eye view at dawn of the village nestling under the Downs ; then we see the players awaken in all the widely different circumstances of their various lives, pass the morning, assemble on the field, play their game, united for a few hours, as men should be, by a common purpose – and at night disperse.

DOS PASSOS, John

ORIENT EXPRESS. A book of travel   *No.* 80

This book will be read because, as well as being the temperature chart of an unfortunate sufferer from the travelling disease, it deals with places shaken by the heavy footsteps of History, manifesting itself as usual by plague, famine, murder, sudden death and depreciated currency. Underneath, the book is an ode to railroad travel.

DOUGLAS, George

THE HOUSE WITH THE GREEN SHUTTERS.

A novel. With an Introduction by J. B. PRIESTLEY   *No.* 118

This powerful and moving story of life in a small Scots burgh is one of the grimmest studies of realism in all modern fiction. The author flashes a cold and remorseless searchlight upon the back-bitings, jealousies, and intrigues of the townsfolk, and his story stands as a classic antidote to the sentimentalism of the kailyard school.

DUNSTERVILLE, Major-General L. G.

STALKY'S REMINISCENCES
No. 145

'The real Stalky, General Dunsterville, who is so delightful a character that the fictitious Stalky must at times feel jealous of him as a rival. . . . In war he proved his genius in the Dunster Force adventure ; and in this book he shows that he possesses another kind of genius – the genius of comic self-revelation and burbling anecdote. And the whole story is told in a vein of comedy that would have done credit to Charles Lever.' *The Observer*

FARSON, Negley

SAILING ACROSS EUROPE. With an Introduction
by FRANK MORLEY
No. 111

A voyage of six months in a ship, its one and only cabin measuring 8 feet by 6 feet, up the Rhine, down the Danube, passing from one to the other by the half-forgotten Ludwig's Canal. To think of and plan such a journey was a fine imaginative effort and to write about it interestingly is no mean accomplishment.

FAUSSET, Hugh I'Anson

TENNYSON. A critical study
No. 124

Mr. Fausset's study of Tennyson's qualities as poet, man, and moralist is by implication a study of some of the predominant characteristics of the Victorian age. His book, however, is as pictorial as it is critical, being woven, to quote *The Times*, 'like an arras of delicate colour and imagery.'

FLAUBERT, Gustave

MADAME BOVARY. Translated by ELEANOR MARX-AVELING. With an Introduction by PERCY LUBBOCK.
No. 144

'. . . It remains perpetually the novel of all novels which the criticism of fiction cannot overlook ; as soon as ever we speak of the principles of the art we must be prepared to engage with Flaubert. There is no such book as his *Bovary* ; for it is a novel in which the subject stands firm and clear, without the least shade of ambiguity to break the line which bounds it.' PERCY LUBBOCK *in The Craft of Fiction*

FORMAN, Henry James
GRECIAN ITALY. A book of Travel *No. 29*

'It has been said that if you were shown Taormina in a vision you would not believe it. If the reader has been in Grecian Italy before he reads this book, the magic of its pages will revive old memories and induce a severe attack of nostalgia.' *From the Preface by* H. FESTING JONES

GARNETT, Edward
FRIDAY NIGHTS. Critical Essays *No. 119*

'Mr. Garnett is "the critic as artist," sensitive alike to elemental nature and the subtlest human variations. His book sketches for us the possible outlines of a new humanism, a fresh valuation of both life and art.' *The Times*

GARNETT, Mrs. R. S.
THE INFAMOUS JOHN FRIEND. A Novel *No. 53*

This book, though in form an historical novel, claims to rank as a psychological study. It is an attempt to depict a character which, though destitute of the common virtues of everyday life, is gifted with qualities that compel love and admiration.

GAUGIN, Paul
THE INTIMATE JOURNALS. Translated by
VAN WYCK BROOKS *No. 101*

The confessions of genius are usually startling ; and Gaugin's *Journals*, now made accessible to the wider world, are no exception. He exults in his power to give free rein to his savage spirit, tearing the shawl from convention's shoulders with a gesture as unscrupulous as it is Rabelaisian.

GIBBS, J. Arthur
A COTSWOLD VILLAGE *No. 138*

'For pure observation of people, places and sports, occupations and wild life, the book is admirable. Everything is put down freshly from the notebook, and has not gone through any deadening process of being written up. There are stories, jokes, snatches of conversation, quotations from old diaries, odds and ends of a hundred kinds about squires, gamekeepers, labourers and their wives.' *Morning Post*

GOBINEAU, Comte de

THE CRIMSON HANDKERCHIEF, AND OTHER STORIES. Translated from the French by HENRY LONGAN STUART
No. 137

The three stories included in this volume mark the flood tide of Comte de Gobineau's unique and long-neglected genius. Not even Nietzsche has surpassed him in a love of heroic characters and unfettered wills – or in his contempt for bourgeois virtues and vices.

GOSSE, Sir Edmund

SELECTED ESSAYS. First Series
No. 73

'The prose of Sir Edmund Gosse is as rich in the colour of young imagination as in the mellow harmony of judgment. Sir Edmund Gosse's literary kit-kats will continue to be read with avidity long after the greater part of the academic criticism of the century is swept away upon the lumber-heap.' *Daily Telegraph*

SELECTED ESSAYS. Second Series
No. 81

A second volume of essays personally chosen by Sir Edmund Gosse from the wild field of his literary work. One is delighted with the width of his appreciation which enables him to write with equal charm on *Wycherley* and on *How to Read the Bible*.

GRAHAM, Stephen

A PRIVATE IN THE GUARDS
No. 89

In his own experiences as a soldier Stephen Graham has conserved the half-forgotten emotions of a nation in arms. Above all, he makes us feel the stark brutality and horror of actual war, the valour which is more than valour, and the disciplined endurance which is human and therefore the more terrifying.

HEARN, Lafcadio

GLEANINGS IN BUDDHA-FIELDS
No. 42

A book which is readable from the first page to the last, and is full of suggestive thought, the essays on Japanese religious belief calling for special praise for the earnest spirit in which the subject is approached.

12

HEARN, Lafcadio

GLIMPSES OF UNFAMILIAR JAPAN. First Series
No. 57

Most books written about Japan have been superficial sketches of a passing traveller. Of the inner life of the Japanese we know practically nothing, their religion, superstitions, ways of thought. Lafcadio Hearn reveals something of the people and their customs as they are.

GLIMPSES OF UNFAMILIAR JAPAN. Second Series
No. 58

Sketches by an acute observer and a master of English prose, of a Nation in transition – of the lingering remains of Old Japan, to-day only a memory, of its gardens, its beliefs, customs, gods and devils, of its wonderful kindliness and charm – and of the New Japan, struggling against odds towards new ideals.

KWAIDAN. Stories
No. 44

The marvellous tales which Mr. Hearn has told in this volume illustrate the wonder-living tendency of the Japanese. The stories are of goblins, fairies and sprites, with here and there an adventure into the field of unveiled supernaturalism.

OUT OF THE EAST
No. 43

Mr. Hearn has written many books about Japan ; he is saturated with the essence of its beauty, and in this book the light and colour and movement of that land drips from his pen in every delicately conceived and finely written sentence.

HEYWARD, Du Bose

PORGY. A Tale
No. 85

This fascinating book gives a vivid and intimate insight into the lives of a group of American negroes, from whom Porgy stands out, rich in humour and tragedy. The author's description of a hurricane is reminiscent in its power.

HILDEBRAND, Arthur Sturges

BLUE WATER. The story of an ocean voyage
No. 36

This book gives the real feeling of life on a small cruising yacht ; the nights on deck with the sails against the sky, long fights with head winds by mountainous coasts to safety in forlorn little island ports, and constant adventure free from care.

HOUSMAN, Laurence

ANGELS AND MINISTERS, AND OTHER
PLAYS. *No. 17*

Imaginary portraits of political characters done in dialogue –
Queen Victoria, Disraeli, Gladstone, Parnell, Joseph Chamberlain
and Woodrow Wilson.

'It is all so good that one is tempted to congratulate Mr. Housman
on a true masterpiece.' *Times*

HUDDLESTON, Sisley

FRANCE AND THE FRENCH. A study *No. 86*

'There has been nothing of its kind published since the war. His
book is a repository of facts marshalled with judgment ; as such
it should assist in clearing away a whole maze of misconceptions
and prejudices, and serve as a sort of pocket encyclopædia of
modern France.' *Times Literary Supplement*

HUDSON, W. H.

MEN, BOOKS AND BIRDS : Letters to a Friend. With
Notes, some Letters, and an Introduction by MORLEY
ROBERTS *No. 112*

An important collection of letters from the naturalist to his friend,
literary executor and fellow author, Morley Roberts, covering a
period of twenty-five years.

JEWETT, Sarah Orne

THE COUNTRY OF THE POINTED FIRS. Stories *No. 28*

'The young student of American literature in the far distant future
will take up this book and say "a masterpiece !" as proudly as if
he had made it. It will be a message in a universal language – the
one message that even the scythe of Time spares.' *From the Preface
by* WILLA CATHER

JONES, Henry Festing

DIVERSIONS IN SICILY. Travel impressions *No. 120*

Shortly before his sudden and unexpected death, Mr. Festing Jones
chose out *Diversions in Sicily* for reprinting in the Travellers'
Library from among his three books of mainly Sicilian sketches
and studies. These chapters, as well as any that he wrote, recapture the wisdom, charm and humour of their author.

JOYCE, James

DUBLINERS. A volume of Stories   *No.* 14

A collection of fifteen short stories by the author of *Ulysses*. They are all of them brave, relentless and sympathetic pictures of Dublin life ; realistic, perhaps, but not crude ; analytical, but not repugnant. No modern writer has greater significance than Mr. Joyce, whose conception and practice of the short story is certainly unique and certainly vital.

KALLAS, Aino

THE WHITE SHIP. Stories. With an Introduction by

JOHN GALSWORTHY   *No.* 24

'The writer has an extraordinary sense of atmosphere.' *Times Literary Supplement*
'Stories told convincingly and well, with a keen perception for natural beauty.' *Nation*

KOMROFF, Manuel

CONTEMPORARIES OF MARCO POLO   *No.* 123

This volume comprises the Travel Records in the Eastern parts of the world of William of Rubruck (1253–5), the Journey of John of Pian de Carpini (1245–7), the Journey of Friar Odoric (1318–30). They describe the marvels and wonders of Asia under the Khans.

THE TRAVELS OF MARCO POLO   *No.* 59

When Marco Polo arrived at the court of the Great Khan, Pekin had just been rebuilt. Kublai Khan was at the height of his glory. Polo rose rapidly in favour and became governor of an important district. In this way he gained first-hand knowledge of a great civilisation and described it with astounding accuracy and detail.

LAWRENCE, A. W., edited by

CAPTIVES OF TIPU. Survivors' Narratives   *No.* 125

Three records of heroic endurance, which were hitherto unobtainable at a reasonable price. In addition to the well-known stories of Bristow and Scurry, a soldier and a seaman, who were forcibly Mohammedanised and retained in the service of Mysore till their escape after ten years, extracts are given from an officer's diary of his close imprisonment at Seringapatam.

15

LAWRENCE, D. H.

TWILIGHT IN ITALY. Travel essays   *No.* 19

This volume of travel vignettes in North Italy was first published in 1916. Since then Mr. Lawrence has increased the number of his admirers year by year. In *Twilight in Italy* they will find all the freshness and vigour of outlook which they have come to expect from its author.

LAWSON, Henry

WHILE THE BILLY BOILS. First Series   *No.* 38

These stories are written by the O. Henry of Australia. They tell of men and dogs, of cities and plains, of gullies and ridges, of sorrow and happiness, and of the fundamental goodness that is hidden in the most unpromising of human soil.

WHILE THE BILLY BOILS. Second Series   *No.* 39

Mr. Lawson has the uncanny knack of making the people he writes about almost violently alive. Whether he tells of jackeroos, bush children or drovers' wives, each one lingers in the memory long after we have closed the book.

LESLIE, Shane

THE END OF A CHAPTER   *No.* 110

In this, his most famous book, Mr. Shane Leslie has preserved for future generations the essence of the pre-war epoch, its institutions and individuals. He writes of Eton, of the Empire, of Post-Victorianism, of the Politicians. . . . And whatever he touches upon, he brilliantly interprets.

LITHGOW, William

RARE ADVENTURES AND PAINEFULL PEREGRINATIONS (1582–1645). Edited and with
Introduction by B. I. LAWRENCE   *No.* 109

This is the book of a seventeenth-century Scotchman who walked over the Levant, North Africa and most of Europe, including Spain, where he was tortured by the Inquisition. An unscrupulous man, full of curiosity, his comments are diverting aad penetrating, his adventures remarkable.

LUBBOCK, Percy

EARLHAM. A portrait *No. 6*

'The book seems too intimate to be reviewed. We want to be allowed to read it, and to dream over it, and keep silence about it. His judgment is perfect, his humour is true and ready ; his touch light and prim ; his prose is exact and clean and full of music.' *Times*

ROMAN PICTURES. Studies *No. 21*

Pictures of life as it is lived – or has been or might be lived – among the pilgrims and colonists in Rome of more or less English speech. 'A book of whimsical originality and exquisite workmanship, and worthy of one of the best prose writers of our time.' *Sunday Times*

THE CRAFT OF FICTION. Critical essays *No. 5*

'No more substantial or more charming volume of criticism has been published in our time.' *Observer*
'To say that this is the best book on the subject is probably true ; but it is more to the point to say that it is the only one.' *Times Literary Supplement*

LYND, Robert

BOOKS AND AUTHORS. Critical essays *No. 135*

Critical essays on great writers of modern and other times. Among the modern writers we have appreciations of Mr. Max Beerbohm, Mr. Arnold Bennett and Mr. H. M. Tomlinson, while Herrick, Keats, Charles Lamb and Hawthorne are a few of the classical writers who are criticised in the book.

MACDONALD, The Rt. Hon. J. Ramsay

WANDERINGS AND EXCURSIONS. Essays *No. 132*

Mr. Ramsay MacDonald has been a wide traveller and reader, and has an uncommon power of bringing an individual eye – the eye of the artist – to bear upon whatever he sees.

17

MACHEN, Arthur

DOG AND DUCK. Essays   *No.* 15

'As a literary artist, Mr. Arthur Machen has few living equals, and that is very far indeed from being his only, or even his greatest, claim on the suffrages of English readers.' *Sunday Times*

MASEFIELD, John

CAPTAIN MARGARET. A Novel   *No.* 35

'His style is crisp, curt and vigorous. He has the Stevensonian sea-swagger, the Stevensonian sense of beauty and poetic spirit. Mr. Masefield's descriptions ring true and his characters carry conviction.' *The Observer*

MASON, Arthur

THE FLYING BO'SUN. A Tale   *No.* 47

'What makes the book remarkable is the imaginative power which has re-created these events so vividly that even the supernatural ones come with the shock and the conviction with which actual supernatural events might come.' *From the Introduction by* EDWIN MUIR

WIDE SEAS AND MANY LANDS. Reminiscences.
With an Introduction by MAURICE BARING   *No.* 7

'This is an extremely entertaining, and at the same time moving, book. We are in the presence of a born writer. We read with the same mixture of amazement and delight that fills us throughout a Conrad novel.' *New Statesman*

MAUGHAM, W. Somerset

LIZA OF LAMBETH. A Tale   *No.* 141

Liza of Lambeth is W. Somerset Maugham's first novel, and its publication decided the whole course of his life. For if it had not succeeded its author could not have turned from medicine to letters, and his subsequent triumphs might never have been achieved. Originally published in 1897, it has since passed through eight editions before its present inclusion in the Travellers' Library. The story reflects much of the experience which Mr. Maugham gathered when he worked in the slums of the East End as a doctor.

MURRY, J. Middleton

THE EVOLUTION OF AN INTELLECTUAL   *No.* 62

These essays were written during and immediately after the Great War. The author says that they record the painful stages by which he passed from the so-called intellectual state to the state of being what he now considers to be a reasonable man.

O'FLAHERTY, Liam

SPRING SOWING. Stories   *No.* 26

'Nothing seems to escape Mr. O'Flaherty's eye ; his brain turns all things to drama ; and his vocabulary is like a river in spate. *Spring Sowing* is a book to buy, or to borrow, or, yes, to steal.' *Bookman*

THE BLACK SOUL. A Novel   *No.* 99

'*The Black Soul* overwhelms one like a storm. . . . Nothing like it has been written by any Irish writer.' 'Æ' in *The Irish Statesman*

THE INFORMER. A Novel   *No.* 128

This realistic novel of the Dublin underworld is generally conceded to be Mr. O'Flaherty's most outstanding book. It is to be produced as a film by British International Pictures, who regard it as one of the most ambitious of their efforts.

O'NEILL, Eugene

THE MOON OF THE CARIBBEES, AND OTHER PLAYS OF THE SEA. With an Introduction by
ST. JOHN ERVINE   *No.* 116

'Mr. O'Neill is immeasurably the most interesting man of letters that America has produced since the death of Walt Whitman.' *From the Introduction*

O'SHAUGHNESSY, Edith

VIENNESE MEDLEY. A Novel   *No.* 51

'It is told with infinite tenderness, with many touches of grave or poignant humour, in a very beautiful book, which no lover of fiction should allow to pass unread. A book which sets its writer definitely in the first rank of living English novelists.' *Sunday Times*

MAUGHAM, W. Somerset

ON A CHINESE SCREEN. Sketches   *No.* 31

A collection of sketches of life in China. Mr. Somerset Maugham writes with equal certainty and vigour whether his characters are Chinese or European. There is a tenderness and humour about the whole book which makes the reader turn eagerly to the next page for more.

THE CASUARINA TREE. Stories   *No.* 92

Intensely dramatic stories in which the stain of the East falls deeply on the lives of English men and women. Mr. Maugham remains cruelly aloof from his characters. On passion and its culminating tragedy he looks with unmoved detachment, ringing the changes without comment and yet with little cynicism.

THE MOON AND SIXPENCE. A Novel   *No.* 9

A remarkable picture of a genius.
'Mr. Maugham has given us a ruthless and penetrating study in personality with a savage truthfulness of delineation and an icy contempt for the heroic and the sentimental.' *The Times*

MENCKEN, H. L.

IN DEFENCE OF WOMEN   *No.* 50

'All I design by the book is to set down in more or less plain form certain ideas that practically every civilised man and woman hold *in petto*, but that have been concealed hitherto by the vast mass of sentimentalities swathing the whole woman question.' *From the Author's Introduction*

SELECTED PREJUDICES. First Series. A Book of Essays   *No.* 8

'He is exactly the kind of man we are needing, an iconoclast, a scoffer at ideals, a critic with whips and scorpions who does not hesitate to deal with literary, social and political humbugs in the one slashing fashion.' *English Review*

SELECTED PREJUDICES. Second Series   *No.* 60

'What a master of the straight left in appreciation ! Everybody who wishes to see how common sense about books and authors can be made exhilarating should acquire this delightful book.' *Morning Post*

MEYNELL, Alice

WAYFARING. Essays   *No.* 133

'Her essays have the merit of saying just enough of the subject, and they can be read repeatedly. The surprise coming from that combined grace of manner and sanity of thought is like one's dream of what the recognition of a new truth would be.' Some of the essays so described by George Meredith are here collected in book-form for the first time.

MITCHISON, Naomi

CLOUD CUCKOO LAND. A Novel of Sparta   *No.* 88

'Rich and frank in passions, and rich, too, in the detail which helps to make feigned life seemed real.' *Times Literary Supplement*

THE CONQUERED. A story of the Gauls under Cæsar   *No.* 45

'With *The Conquered* Mrs. Mitchison establishes herself as the best, if not the only, English historical novelist now writing. It seems to me in many respects the most attractive and poignant historical novel I have ever read.' *New Statesman*

WHEN THE BOUGH BREAKS. Stories of the time
when Rome was crumbling to ruin   *No.* 46

'Interesting, delightful and fresh as morning dew. The connoisseur in short stories will turn to some pages in this volume again and again with renewed relish.' *Times Literary Supplement*

MONTAGU, Lady Mary Wortley

THE TRAVEL LETTERS OF LADY MARY
WORTLEY MONTAGU. Edited by A. W. LAWRENCE *No.* 143

The famous account of Lady Mary's journey to the East in 1716, describing her visits to the German Courts and her residence in Constantinople. In the words of a review by Tobias Smollett : 'The publication of these *Letters* will be an immortal monument to the memory of Lady Mary Wortley Montagu and will show, as long as the English language endures, the sprightliness of her wit, the solidity of her judgment, the elegance of her taste, and the excellence of her real character. These letters are so bewitchingly entertaining, that we defy the most phlegmatic man on earth to read one without going through with them.'

20

MOORE, George

CONFESSIONS OF A YOUNG MAN   *No.* 76

'Mr. Moore, true to his period and to his genius, stripped himself of everything that might stand between him and the achievement of his artistic object. He does not ask you to admire this George Moore. He merely asks you to observe him beyond good and evil as a constant plucked from the bewildering flow of eternity.' *Humbert Wolfe*

MORLEY, Christopher

SAFETY PINS. Essays. With an Introduction by H.M.
TOMLINSON   *No.* 98

Very many readers will be glad of the opportunity to meet Mr Morley in the rôle of the gentle essayist. He is an author who is content to move among his fellows, to note, to reflect, and to write genially and urbanely ; to love words for their sound as well as for their value in expression of thought.

THUNDER ON THE LEFT. A Novel   *No.* 90

'It is personal to every reader, it will become for every one a reflection of himself. I fancy that here, as always where work is fine and true, the author has created something not as he would but as he must, and is here an interpreter of a world more wonderful than he himself knows.' *Hugh Walpole*

WHERE THE BLUE BEGINS. A Fantasy   *No.* 74

A delicious satirical fantasy in which humanity wears a dog-collar. 'Mr. Morley is a master of consequent inconsequence. His humour and irony are excellent, and his satire is only the more salient for the delicate and ingenuous fantasy in which it is set.' *Manchester Guardian*

MURRAY, Max

THE WORLD'S BACK DOORS. Adventures. With
an Introduction by HECTOR BOLITHO   *No.* 61

This book is not an account so much of places as of people. The journey round the world was begun with about enough money to buy one meal, and continued for 66,000 miles. There are periods as a longshore man and as a sailor, and a Chinese guard and a night watchman, and as a hobo.

21

PATER, Walter

MARIUS THE EPICUREAN   *No. 23*

Walter Pater was at the same time a scholar of wide sympathies and a master of the English language. In this, his best-known work, he describes with rare delicacy of feeling and insight the religious and philosophic tendencies of the Roman Empire at the time of Antoninus Pius as they affected the mind and life of the story's hero.

THE RENAISSANCE   *No. 63*

This English classic contains studies of those 'supreme artists' Michelangelo and Da Vinci, and of Botticelli, Della Robia, Mirandola, and others, who 'have a distinct faculty of their own by which they convey to us a peculiar quality of pleasure which we cannot get elsewhere.' There is no romance or subtlety in the work of these masters too fine for Pater to distinguish in superb English.

PICKTHALL, Marmaduke

ORIENTAL ENCOUNTERS   *No. 103*

In *Oriental Encounters*, Mr. Pickthall relives his earlier manhood's discovery of Arabia and sympathetic encounters with the Eastern mind. He is one of the few travellers who really bridges the racial gulf.

POWELL, Sydney Walter

THE ADVENTURES OF A WANDERER   *No. 64*

Throwing up a position in the Civil Service in Natal because he preferred movement and freedom to monotony and security, the author started his wanderings by enlisting in an Indian Ambulance Corps in the South African War. Afterwards he wandered all over the world.

POWYS, Llewelyn

BLACK LAUGHTER   *No. 127*

Black Laughter is a kind of *Robinson Crusoe* of the continent of Africa. Indeed, Llewelyn Powys resembles Daniel Defoe in the startlingly realistic manner in which he conveys the actual feelings of the wild places he describes. You actually share the sensations of a sensitive and artistic nature suddenly transplanted from a peaceful English village into the heart of Africa.

RANSOME, Arthur
'RACUNDRA'S' FIRST CRUISE
No. 65

This is the story of the building of an ideal yacht which would be a cruising boat that one man could manage if need be, but on which three people could live comfortably. The adventures of the cruise are skilfully and vividly told.

READE, Winwood
THE MARTYRDOM OF MAN
No. 66

'Few sketches of universal history by one single author have been written. One book that has influenced me very strongly is *The Martyrdom of Man*. This "dates," as people say nowadays, and it has a fine gloom of its own ; but it is still an extraordinarily inspiring presentation of human history as one consistent process.' H. G. WELLS *in An Outline of History*

REYNOLDS, Stephen
A POOR MAN'S HOUSE
No. 93

Vivid and intimate pictures of a Devonshire fisherman's life. 'Compact, harmonious, without a single – I won't say false – but uncertain note, true in aim, sentiment and expression, precise and imaginative, never precious, but containing here and there an absolutely priceless phrase. . . .' *Joseph Conrad*

RIESENBERG, Felix
SHIPMATES. Sea-faring portraits
No. 107

A collection of intimate character-portraits of men with whom the author has sailed on many voyages. The sequence of studies blends into a fascinating panorama of living characters.

ROBERTS, Captain George
THE FOUR YEARS VOYAGES
No. 40

The Manner of his being taken by Three Pyrate Ships which, after having plundered him, and detained him 10 Days, put him aboard his own Sloop, without Provisions, Water, etc.
The Hardships he endur'd for above 20 Days, 'till he arriv'd at the Island of St. Nicholas, from whence he was blown off to Sea ; and after Four Days of Difficulty and Distress, was Shipwreck'd on the Unfrequented Island of St. John, where, after he had remained near two Years, he built a Vessel to bring himself off.

ROBINSON, James Harvey

THE MIND IN THE MAKING. An Essay   *No. 9*

'For me, I think James Harvey Robinson is going to be almost as important as was Huxley in my adolescence, and William James in later years. It is a cardinal book. I question whether in the long run people may not come to it, as making a new initiative into the world's thought and methods.' *From the Introduction by* H. G. WELLS

ROSEBERY, The Earl of

NAPOLEON : THE LAST PHASE   *No. 96*

Of books and memoirs about Napoleon there is indeed no end, but of the veracious books such as this there are remarkably few. It aims to penetrate the deliberate darkness which surrounds the last act of the Napoleonic drama.

RUTHERFORD, Mark

THE AUTOBIOGRAPHY OF MARK RUTHERFORD.
With an Introduction by H. W. MASSINGHAM   *No. 67*

Because of its honesty, delicacy and simplicity of portraiture, this book has always had a curious grip upon the affections of its readers. An English Amiel, inheriting to his comfort an English Old Crome landscape, he freed and strengthened his own spirit as he will his reader's.

THE DELIVERANCE   *No. 68*

Once read, Hale White [Mark Rutherford] is never forgotten. But he is not yet approached through the highways of English letters. To the lover of his work, nothing can be more attractive than the pure and serene atmosphere of thought in which his art moves.

THE REVOLUTION IN TANNER'S LANE   *No. 69*

'Since Bunyan, English Puritanism has produced one imaginative genius of the highest order. To my mind, our fiction contains no more perfectly drawn pictures of English life in its recurring emotional contrast of excitement and repose more valuable to the historian, or more stimulating to the imaginative reader.' *H. W. Massingham*

SHELVOCKE, Captain George

A PRIVATEER'S VOYAGE ROUND THE WORLD.
With aspersions upon him by WILLIAM BETAGH. Edited by
A. W. LAWRENCE   *No.* 142

A book of 1726, well known as the source of the albatross incident
and other passages in the 'Ancient Mariner'; it describes the ex-
ploits of a private ship of war on the coasts of South America, its
wreck on the Crusoe island off Juan Fernandez, and the subsequent
adventures of its company in various parts of the Pacific.

Few among the true stories of the sea can rival this in psychological
interest, because of the diverse villainies of captain and crew.
Shelvocke was arrested on his return to England, for a successful
conspiracy to defraud his owners of their due percentage of the
profits, and he then wrote his book to defend his conduct.

SITWELL, Constance

FLOWERS AND ELEPHANTS. With an Introduction
by E. M. FORSTER   *No.* 115

Mrs. Sitwell has known India well, and has filled her pages with
many vivid little pictures, and with sounds and scents. But it is
the thread on which her impressions are strung that is so fascinating,
a thread so delicate and rare that the slightest clumsiness in defini-
tion would snap it.

SMITH, Pauline

THE BEADLE. A Novel of South Africa   *No.* 129

'A story of great beauty, and told with simplicity and tenderness
that makes it linger in the memory. It is a notable contribution to
the literature of the day.' *Morning Post*

THE LITTLE KAROO. Stories of South Africa. With
an Introduction by ARNOLD BENNETT   *No.* 104

'Nothing like this has been written about South African life since
Olive Schreiner and her *Story of an African Farm* took the literary
world by storm.' *The Daily Telegraph*

SQUIRE, J. C.

THE GRUB STREET NIGHTS ENTERTAINMENTS *No.* 102

Stories of literary life, told with a breath of fantasy and gaily ironic humour. Each character lives, and is the more lively for its touch of caricature. From *The Man Who Kept a Diary* to *The Man Who Wrote Free Verse*, these tales constitute Mr. Squire's most delightful ventures in fiction ; and the conception of the book itself is unique.

SULLIVAN, J. W. N.

ASPECTS OF SCIENCE. First Series *No.* 70

Although they deal with different aspects of various scientific ideas, the papers which make up this volume do illustrate, more or less, one point of view. This book tries to show one or two of the many reasons why science may be interesting for people who are not specialists as well as for those who are.

SYMONS, Arthur

PLAYS, ACTING AND MUSIC *No.* 113

This book deals mainly with music and with the various arts of the stage. Mr. Arthur Symons shows how each art has its own laws, its own limits ; these it is the business of the critic jealously to distinguish. Yet in the study of art as art it should be his endeavour to master the universal science of beauty.

WILLIAM BLAKE. A critical study *No.* 94

When Blake spoke the first word of the nineteenth century there was none to hear it ; and now that his message has penetrated the world, and is slowly remaking it, few are conscious of the man who first voiced it. This lack of knowledge is remedied in Mr. Symons's work.

TCHEKOFF, Anton

TWO PLAYS : *The Cherry Orchard* and *The Sea Gull.*
Translated by GEORGE CALDERON *No.* 33

Tchekoff had that fine comedic spirit which relishes the incongruity between the actual disorder of the world with the underlying order. He habitually mingled tragedy (which is life seen close at hand) with comedy (which is life seen at a distance). His plays are tragedies with the texture of comedy.

27

THOMAS, Edward

A LITERARY PILGRIM IN ENGLAND   *No.* 95

A book about the homes and resorts of English writers, from John Aubrey, Cowper, Gilbert White, Cobbett, Wordsworth, Burns, Borrow and Lamb, to Swinburne, Stevenson, Meredith, W. H. Hudson and H. Belloc. Each chapter is a miniature biography and the same time a picture of the man and his work and environment.

THE POCKET BOOK OF POEMS AND SONGS
FOR THE OPEN AIR   *No.* 97

This anthology is meant to please those lovers of poetry and the country who like a book that can always lighten some of their burdens or give wings to their delight, whether in the open air by day, or under the roof at evening ; in it is gathered much of the finest English poetry.

TURGENEV, Ivan

FATHERS AND CHILDREN. Translated by
CONSTANCE GARNETT   *No.* 83

'As a piece of art *Fathers and Children* is the most powerful of all Turgenev's works. The figure of Bazarov is not only the political centre of the book, but a figure in which the eternal tragedy of man's impotence and insignificance is realised in scenes of a most ironical human drama.' *Edward Garnett*

ON THE EVE. Translated by CONSTANCE GARNETT   *No.* 82

In his characters is something of the width and depth which so astounds us in the creations of Shakespeare. *On the Eve* is a quiet work, yet over which the growing consciousness of coming events casts its heavy shadow. Turgenev, even as he sketched the ripening love of a young girl, has made us feel the dawning aspirations o. a nation.

SMOKE. Translated by CONSTANCE GARNETT   *No.* 84

In this novel Turgenev sees and reflects, even in the shifting phases of political life, that which is universal in human nature. His work is compassionate, beautiful, unique ; in the sight of his fellow-craftsmen always marvellous and often perfect.

VERGA, Giovanni

MASTRO-DON GESUALDO. A Novel. Translated by D. H. LAWRENCE

No. 71

Verga, who died in 1922, is recognised as one of the greatest of Italian writers of fiction. He can claim a place beside Hardy and the Russians. 'It is a fine full tale, a fine full picture of life, with a bold beauty of its own which Mr. Lawrence must have relished greatly as he translated it.' *Observer*

VOIGT, F. A.

COMBED OUT

No. 122

This account of life in the army in 1917-18, both at home and in France, is written with a telling incisiveness. The author does not indulge in an unnecessary word, but packs in just the right details with an intensity of feeling that is infectious.

WATERS, W. G.

TRAVELLER'S JOY. An Anthology

No. 106

This anthology has been selected for publication in the Travellers' Library from among the many collections of verse because of its suitability for the traveller, particularly the summer and autumn traveller, who would like to carry with him some store of literary provender.

WELLS, H. G.

CHRISTINA ALBERTA'S FATHER. A Novel

No. 100

'At first reading the book is utterly beyond criticism ; all the characters are delightfully genuine.' *Spectator*
'Brimming over with Wellsian insight, humour and invention. No one but Mr. Wells could have written the whole book and given it such verve and sparkle.' *Westminster Gazette*

THE DREAM. A Novel

No. 20

'It is the richest, most generous and absorbing thing that Mr. Wells has given us for years and years.' *Daily News*
'I find this book as close to being magnificent as any book that I have ever read. It is full of inspiration and life.' *Daily Graphic*

WHARTON, Edith

IN MOROCCO   *No.* 41

Morocco is a land of mists and mysteries, of trailing silver veils
through which minarets, mighty towers, hot palm groves and Atlas
snows peer and disappear at the will of the Atlantic cloud-drifts.

ITALIAN BACKGROUNDS   *No.* 114

Mrs. Wharton's perception of beauty and her grace of writing are
matters of general acceptance. Her book gives us pictures of
mountains and rivers, monks, nuns and saints.

WITHERS, Percy

FRIENDS IN SOLITUDE. With an Introduction by
LASCELLES ABERCROMBIE   *No.* 131

Percy Withers, who lived for many years in the Lake Country, has
his own experiences to relate ; but in seeking to widen them and to
give them more vivid expression, he selects certain of the dale folk,
his friends and companions, to tell in their own fashion so much the
manner of men they are, so much of their life-story, of its pros-
perities, endurances, pathos, its reactions and responses to the
outward circumstances as may make the picture more complete
and give to it a more human significance.

YOUNG, E. H.

THE MISSES MALLETT. A Novel   *No.* 72

The virtue of this quiet and accomplished piece of writing lies in
its quality and in its character-drawing ; to summarise it would be
to give no idea of its charm. Neither realism nor romance, it is a
book by a writer of insight and sensibility.

WILLIAM. A Novel   *No.* 27

'An extraordinary good book, penetrating and beautiful.' *Allan
Monkhouse*
'All its characters are very real and alive, and William himself is a
masterpiece.' *May Sinclair*

NUMERICAL INDEX TO TITLES

ALPHABETICAL INDEX TO TITLES

Note

The Travellers' Library is published as a joint enterprise by Jonathan Cape and William Heinemann. The series as a whole, or any title in the series, can be ordered through booksellers from either Jonathan Cape or William Heinemann. Booksellers' only care must be not to duplicate their orders.